Sting

C000051077

for *easy guitar* tab

Wise Publications
London / New York / Paris / Sydney / Copenhagen / Madrid

Exclusive Distributors:
Music Sales Limited
8/9 Frith Street, London W1V 5TZ, England.
Music Sales Pty Limited
120 Rothschild Avenue, Rosebery, NSW 2018, Australia.

Order No. AM940500
ISBN 0-7119-6133-6
This book © Copyright 1997 by Wise Publications.

Art direction by Michael Bell Design.
Compiled by Peter Evans.
Music arranged by Andy Jones.
Music edited by Arthur Dick.
Music processed by Seton Music Graphics.

Printed in the United Kingdom by
Redwood Books, Trowbridge, Wiltshire.

Sting cover picture courtesy of:
London Features International

Your Guarantee of Quality:
As publishers, we strive to produce every book to
the highest commercial standards.
The music has been freshly engraved and the book has
been carefully designed to minimise awkward page turns and
to make playing from it a real pleasure.
Particular care has been given to specifying acid-free,
neutral-sized paper made from pulps which have not been
elemental chlorine bleached.
This pulp is from farmed sustainable forests and was produced
with special regard for the environment.
Throughout, the printing and binding have been planned to ensure
a sturdy, attractive publication which should give years of enjoyment.
If your copy fails to meet our high standards, please
inform us and we will gladly replace it.

Music Sales' complete catalogue describes
thousands of titles and is available in full colour sections by
subject, direct from Music Sales Limited.
Please state your areas of interest and send a cheque/
postal order for £1.50 for postage to:
Music Sales Limited, Newmarket Road, Bury St. Edmunds,
Suffolk IP33 3YB.

Visit the Internet Music Shop at
http://www.musicsales.co.uk

Tablature & Instructions Explained

Hello, and welcome to *Sting For Easy Guitar Tab*. Congratulations on buying a book that will improve your playing and provide you with hours of pleasure. All of the songs in this book have been freshly transcribed and arranged by professional guitarist Andy Jones. We trust that his years of experience have resulted in a satisfying publication.

The specially arranged guitar tablature music in this book will enable you to make great music right away, even if you can't read standard music notation. The simple and logical system of tablature, or 'tab', makes it easy to find your way around the guitar fretboard.

You only need to know a few things about tab before we get started. First of all, take a look at the tablature stave. It comprises six lines, each corresponding to one of the strings on the guitar. The bottom line on the stave corresponds to the lowest-pitched string, and so forth.

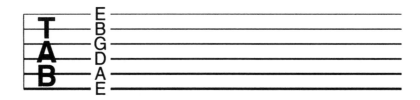

A number on any of these lines tells you at what fret you should play a note.

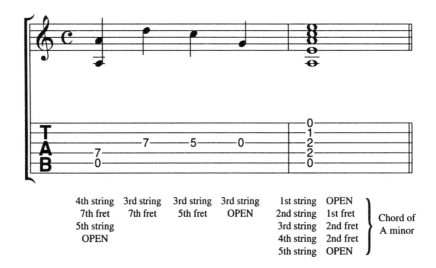

Occasionally in this book you will see two (or more) notes with a little curved line connecting them. This line is called a slur, and two notes connected by a slur constitute what is called either a hammer-on or a pull-off.

A hammer-on is exactly as it sounds. You simply 'hammer' a left-hand finger down on to a string hard enough that it sounds without your having to pluck it with your right-hand finger. Hammer-ons are usually to notes higher than the one you played just before.

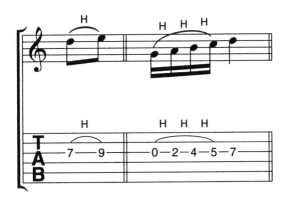

A pull-off is the other side of the coin: you quickly pull your left-hand finger off a fretted string so that a lower note sounds without your having to re-strike it.

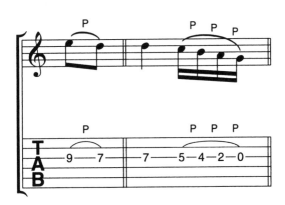

Now you're ready to enjoy the music in this book. A useful tip is to remember that your guitar can only sound as good as the strings you use. Regular cleaning will prolong their life, but professional guitarists change strings after every performance.

An Englishman In New York

Words & Music by Sting

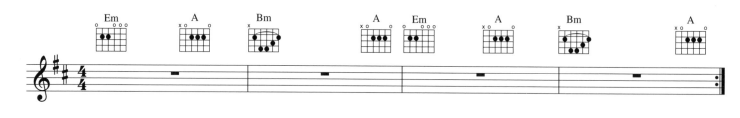

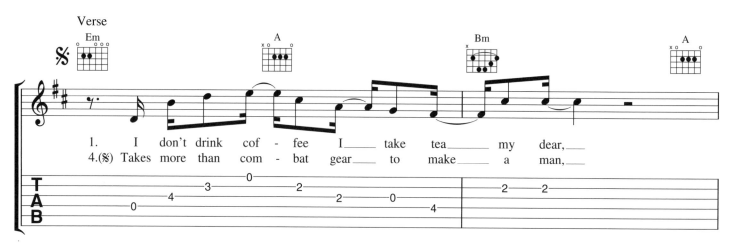

1. I don't drink cof - fee I___ take tea___ my dear,___
4.(%) Takes more than com - bat gear to make___ a man,___

I like my toast___ done on___ one side.___
takes more than a li - cense for___ a gun.___

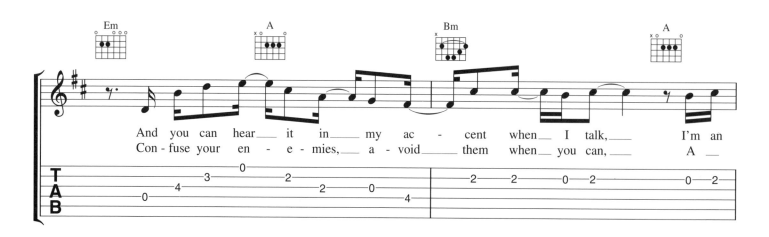

And you can hear___ it in___ my ac - cent when___ I talk,___ I'm an
Con - fuse your en - e - mies,___ a - void___ them when___ you can,___ A___

Eng - lish___ man in New___ York.___
gentle - man___ will walk but nev - er run.

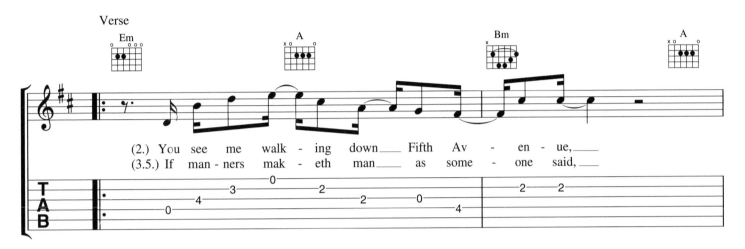

Verse

(2.) You see me walk - ing down___ Fifth Av - en - ue,___
(3.5.) If man - ners mak - eth man___ as some - one said, ___

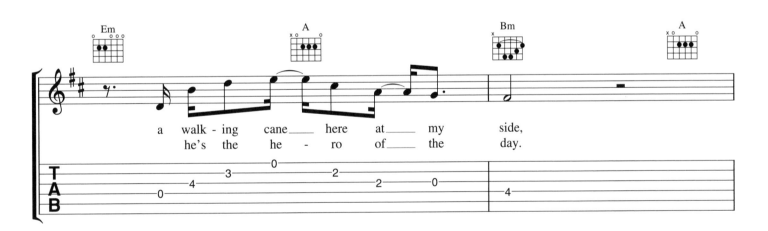

a walk - ing cane___ here at___ my side,
he's the he - ro of___ the day.

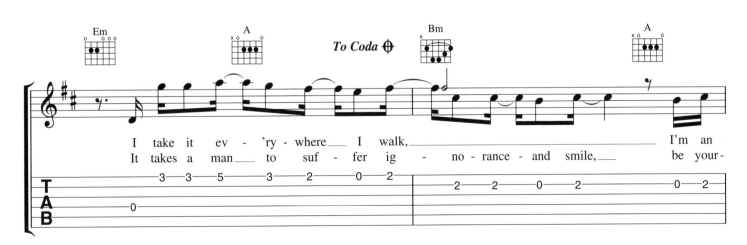

I take it ev - 'ry - where___ I walk,___   I'm an
It takes a man___ to suf - fer ig - no - rance - and smile,___   be your-

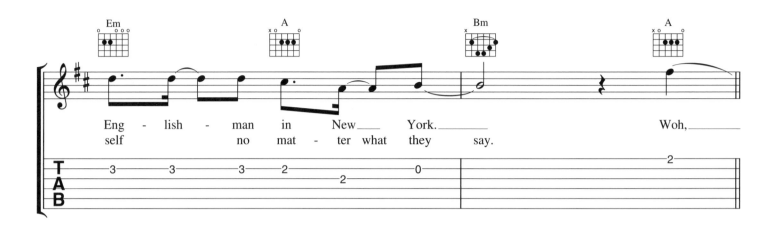

Eng - lish - man in New____ York._____

self no mat - ter what they say.

Woh,_____

Chorus

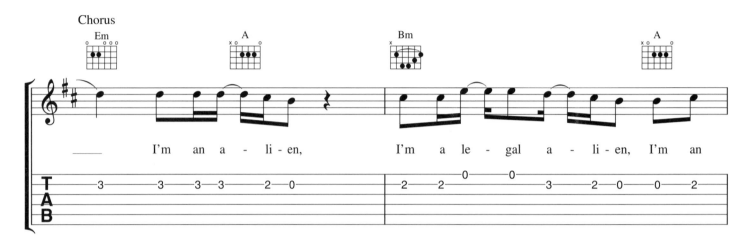

____ I'm an a - li - en, I'm a le - gal a - li - en, I'm an

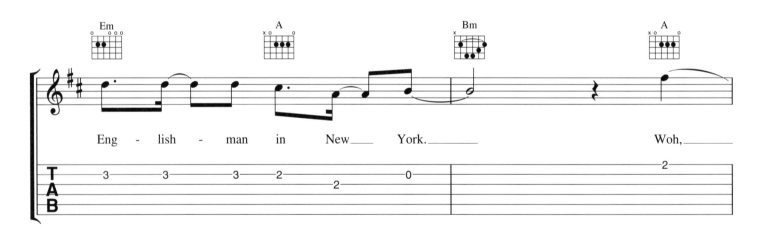

Eng - lish - man in New____ York._____

Woh,_____

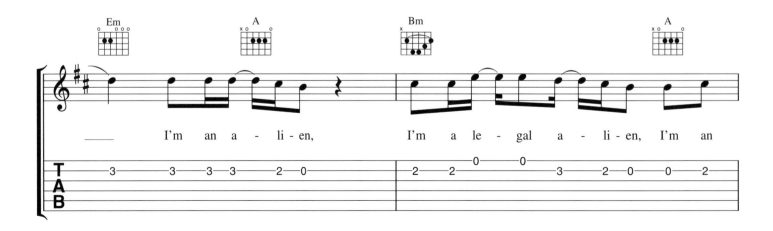

____ I'm an a - li - en, I'm a le - gal a - li - en, I'm an

Eng - lis - man in New__ York._____

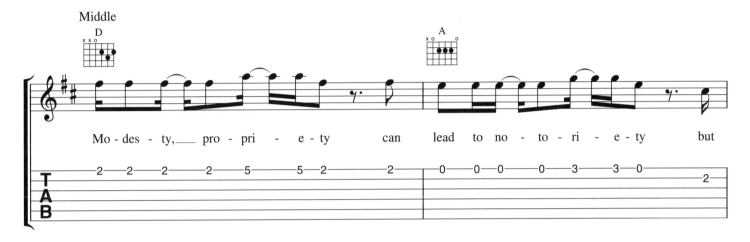

Mo - des - ty,___ pro - pri - e - ty can lead to no - to - ri - e - ty but

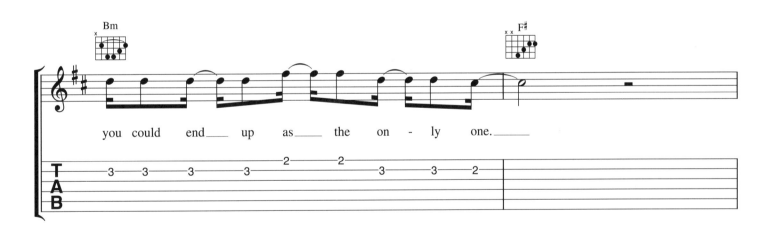

you could end___ up as___ the on - ly one.___

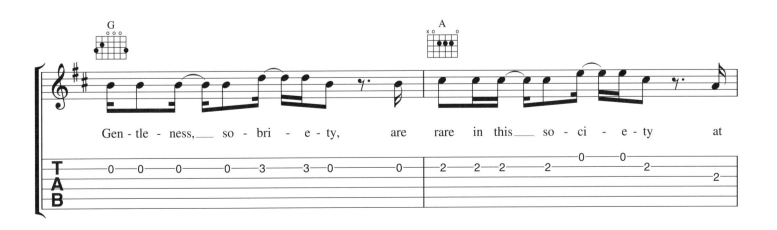

Gen - tle - ness,___ so - bri - e - ty, are rare in this___ so - ci - e - ty at

Can't Stand Losing You

Words & Music by Sting

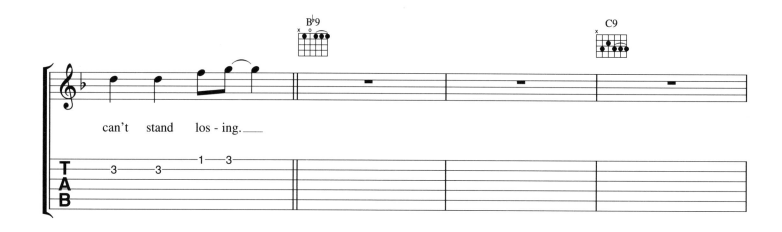

can't stand los - ing.___

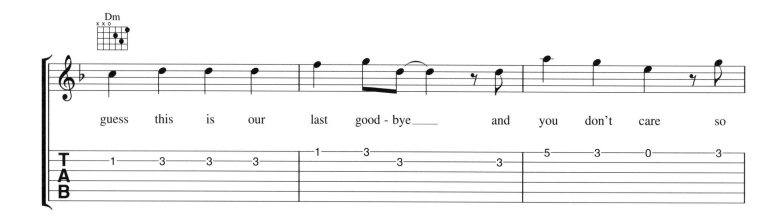

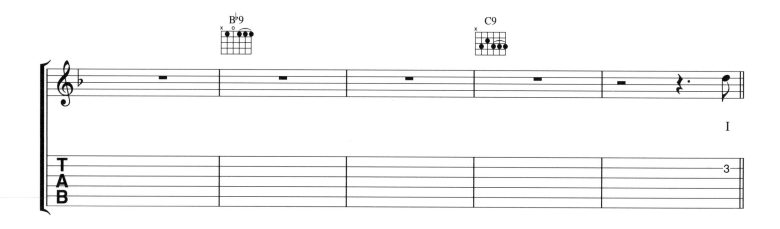

guess this is our last good - bye___ and you don't care so

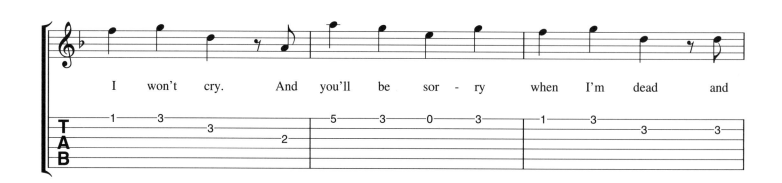

I won't cry. And you'll be sor - ry when I'm dead and

14

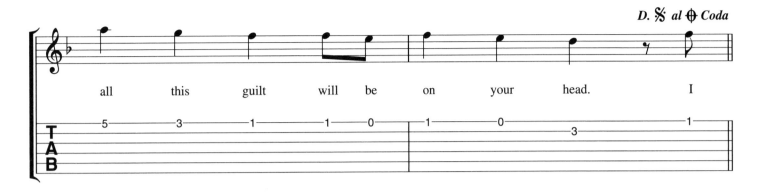

all this guilt will be on your head. I

Coda ⊕

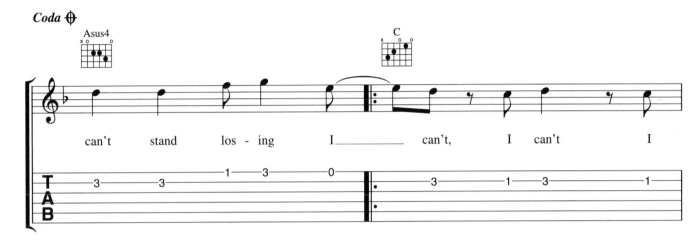

can't stand los - ing I_____ can't, I can't I

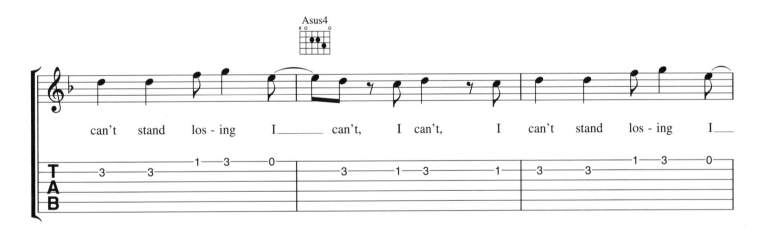

can't stand los - ing I_____ can't, I can't, I can't stand los - ing I_____

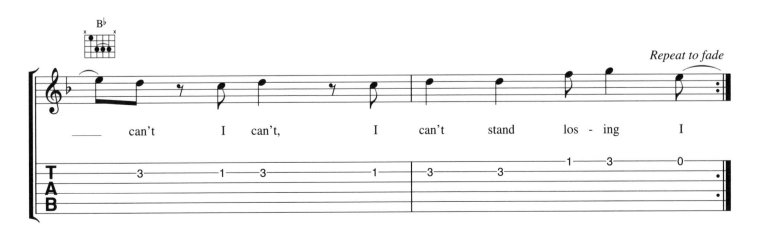

Repeat to fade

_____ can't I can't, I can't stand los - ing I

15

Every Breath You Take

Words & Music by Sting

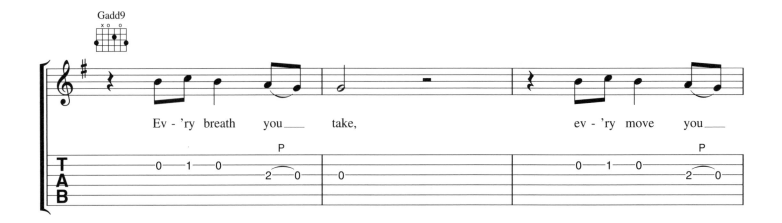

Ev - 'ry breath you___ take,   ev - 'ry move you___

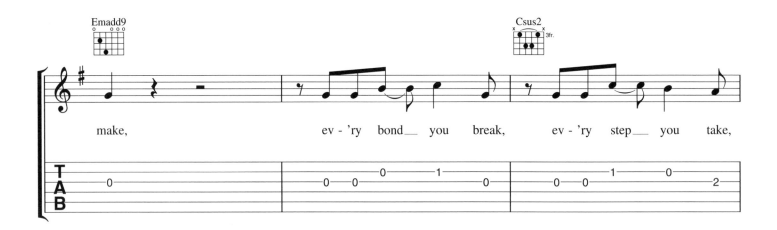

make,   ev - 'ry bond___ you break,   ev - 'ry step___ you take,

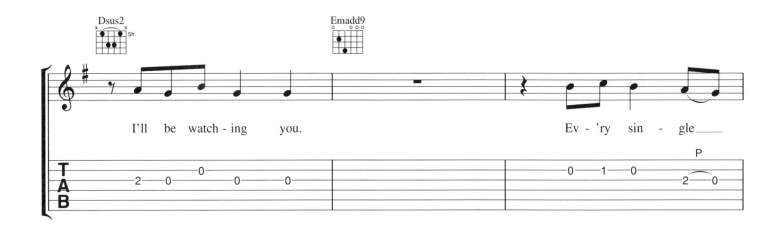

I'll be watch - ing   you.   Ev - 'ry sin - gle___

day,   ev - 'ry word   you____ say,

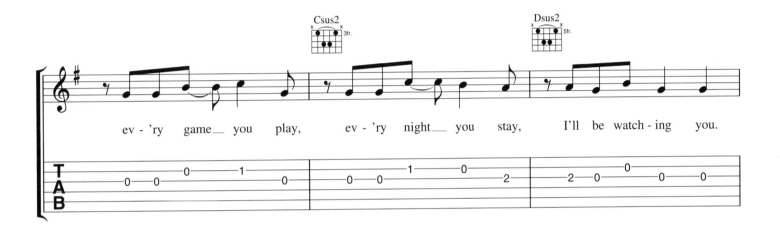

ev - 'ry game__ you   play,   ev - 'ry night__ you   stay,   I'll be watch - ing   you.

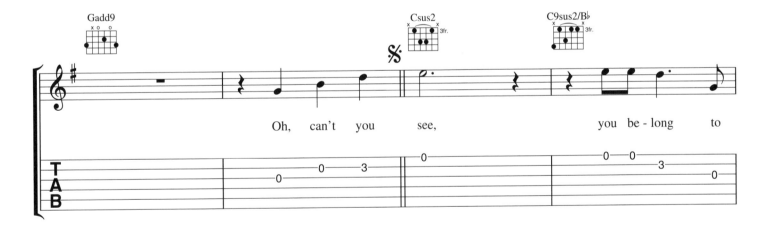

Oh,   can't   you   see,   you be - long   to

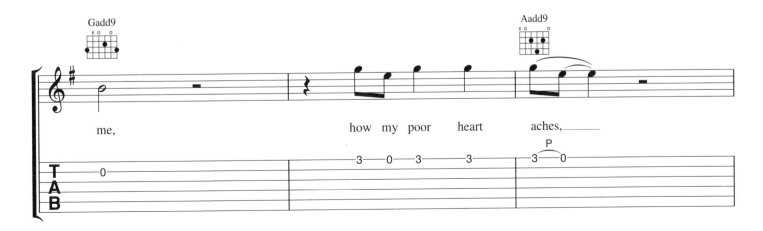

me,   how my poor   heart   aches,____

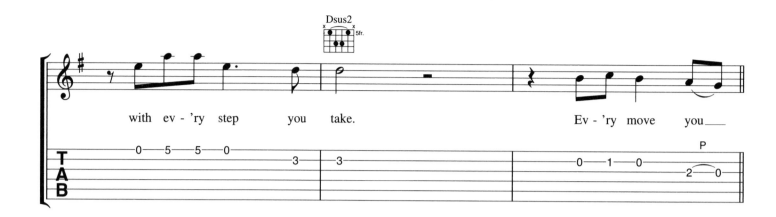

with ev - 'ry step you take.   Ev - 'ry move you___

make,   ev - 'ry vow you___ break,

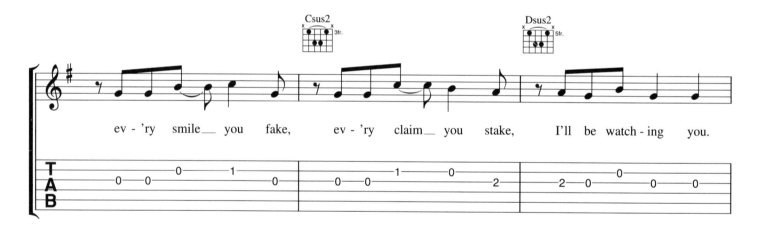

ev - 'ry smile___ you fake,   ev - 'ry claim___ you stake,   I'll be watch - ing you.

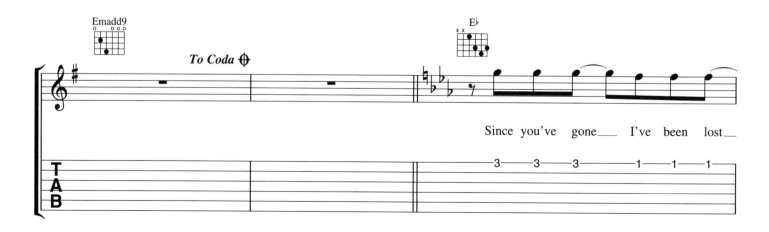

To Coda ⊕

Since you've gone___ I've been lost___

Fields Of Gold

Words & Music by Sting

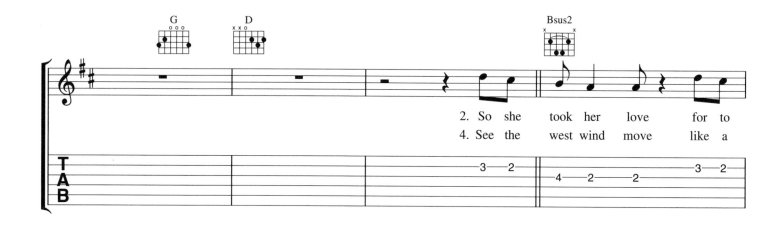

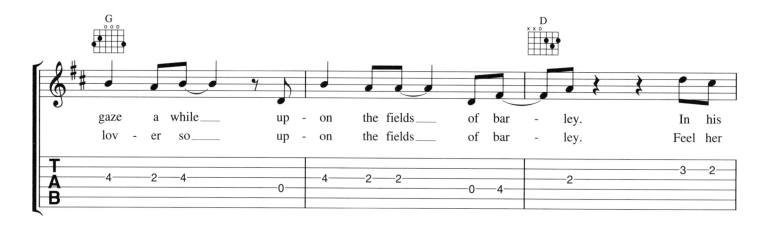

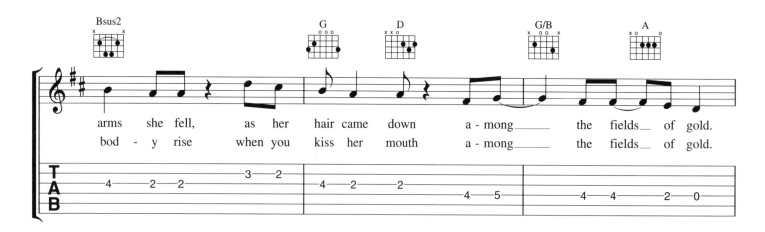

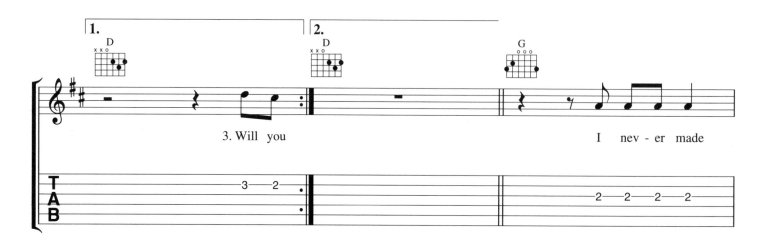

prom - is - es light - ly, and there have been some that I've bro - ken,

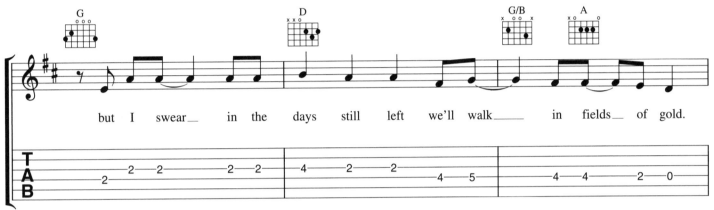

but I swear___ in the days still left we'll walk_____ in fields___ of gold.

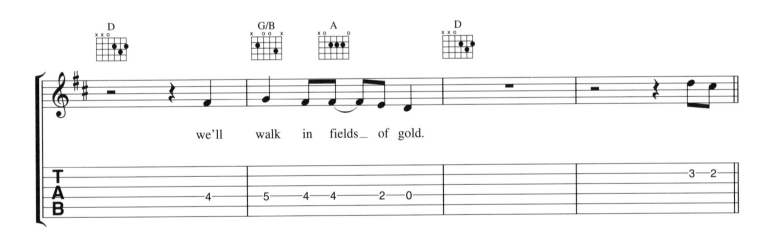

we'll walk in fields___ of gold.

Solo

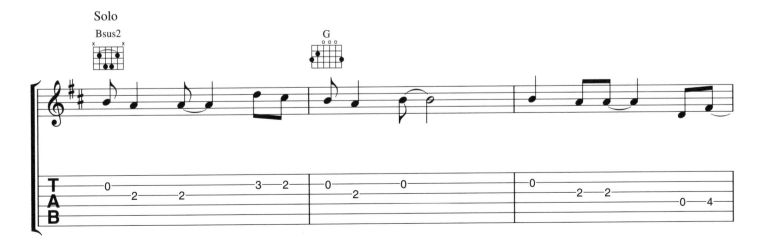

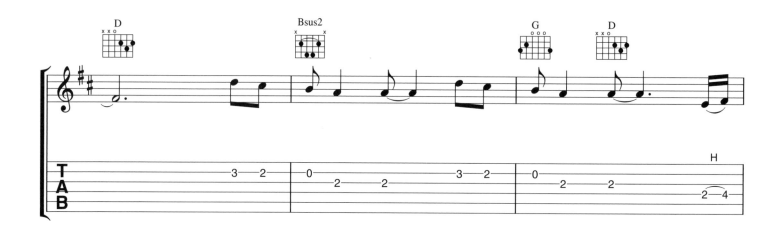

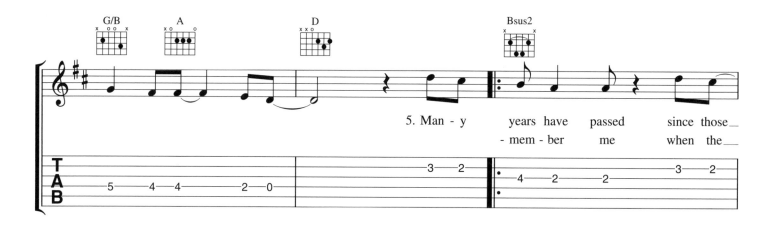

5. Man - y   years have   passed   since those___
- mem - ber   me   when the___

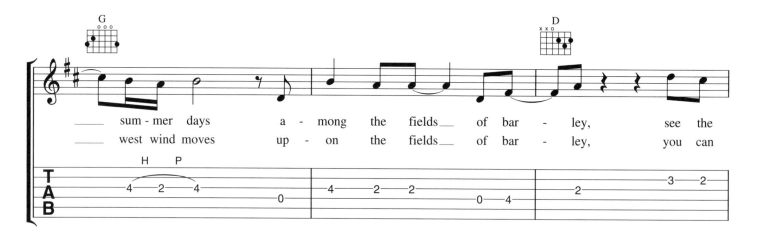

___ sum - mer days   a - mong   the fields___ of bar - ley,   see the
___ west wind moves   up - on   the fields___ of bar - ley,   you can

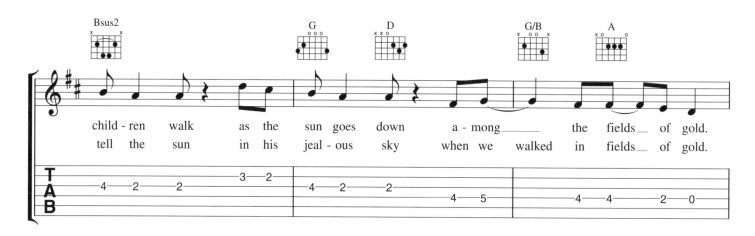

child - ren   walk   as the   sun goes   down   a - mong_____   the fields___ of gold.
tell   the   sun   in his   jeal - ous   sky   when we   walked   in   fields___ of gold.

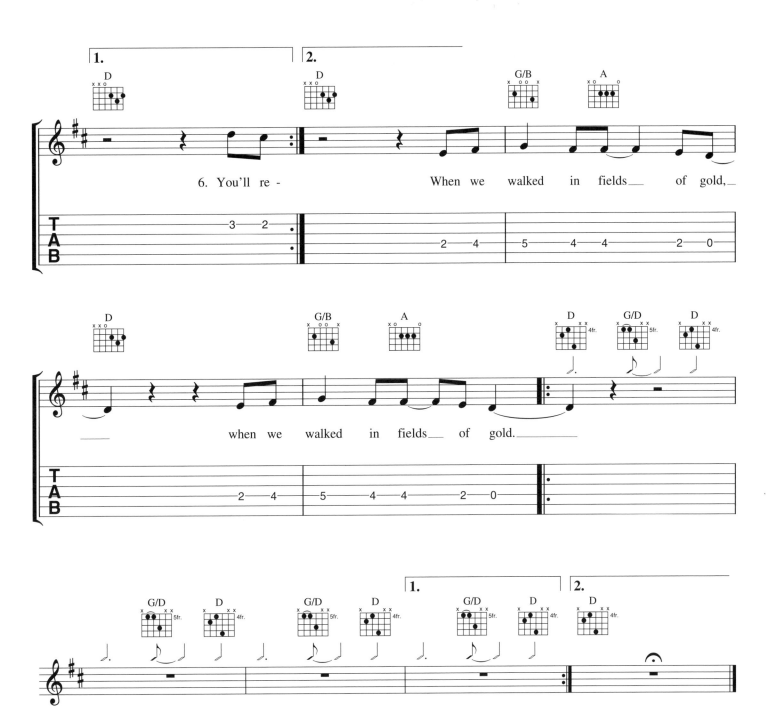

6. You'll re - When we walked in fields___ of gold,___

when we walked in fields___ of gold.___

Heavy Cloud No Rain

Words & Music by Sting

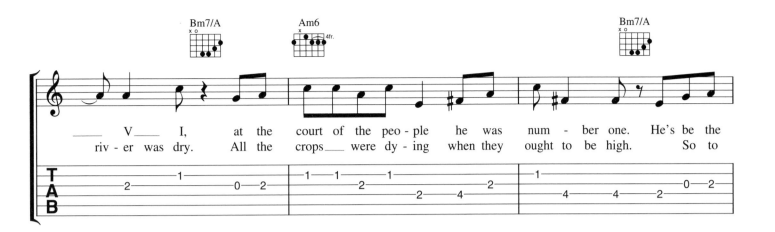

_____ V _____ I, at the court of the peo - ple he was num - ber one. He's be the
riv - er was dry. All the crops___ were dy - ing when they ought to be high. So to

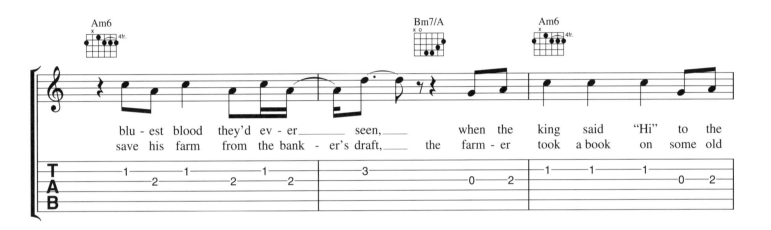

blu - est blood they'd ev - er___ seen,___ when the king said "Hi" to the
save his farm from the bank - er's draft,___ the farm - er took a book on some old

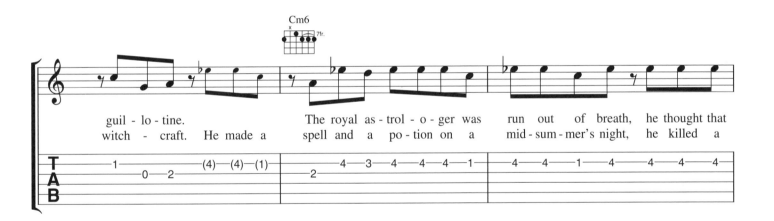

guil - lo - tine. The royal as - trol - o - ger was run out of breath, he thought that
witch - craft. He made a spell and a po - tion on a mid - sum - mer's night, he killed a

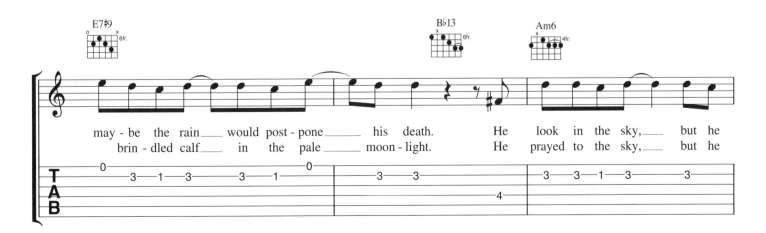

may - be the rain___ would post - pone___ his death. He look in the sky,___ but he
brin - dled calf___ in the pale___ moon - light. He prayed to the sky,___ but he

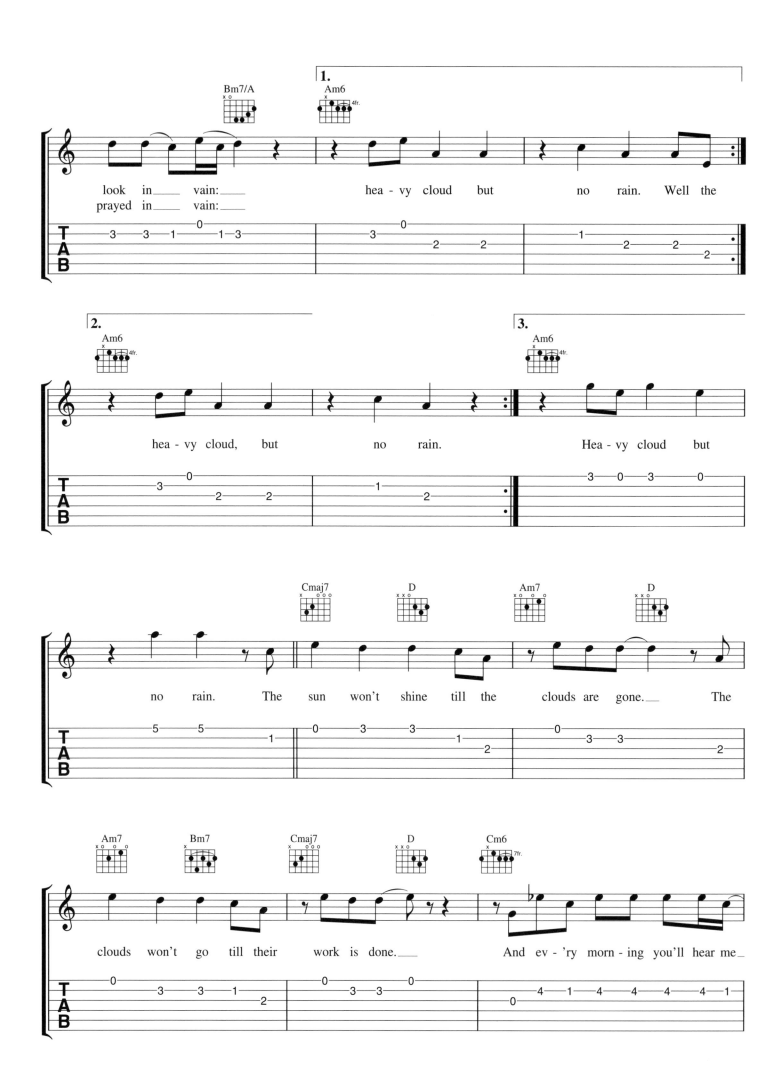

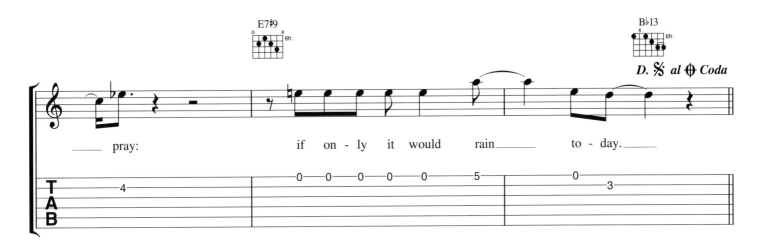

pray: if on - ly it would rain_____ to - day._____

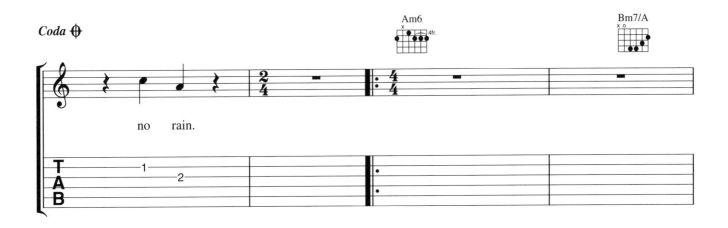

no rain.

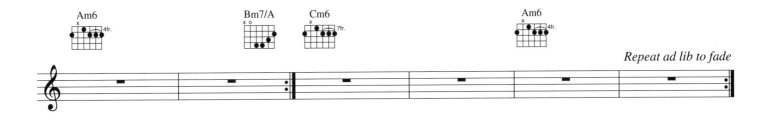

It's Probably Me

Words & Music by Sting, Eric Clapton & Michael Kamen

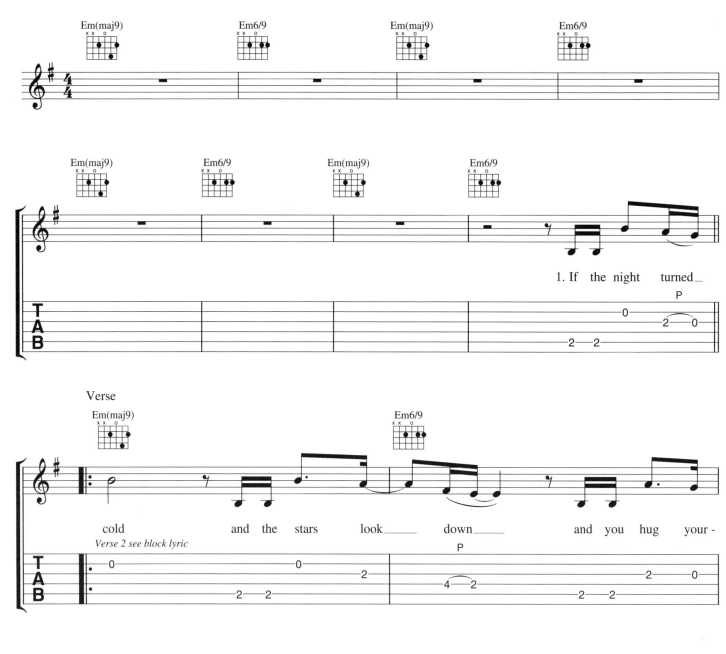

1. If the night turned__

Verse

cold and the stars look__ down__ and you hug your-

Verse 2 see block lyric

self and the cold, cold__ ground, you wake the

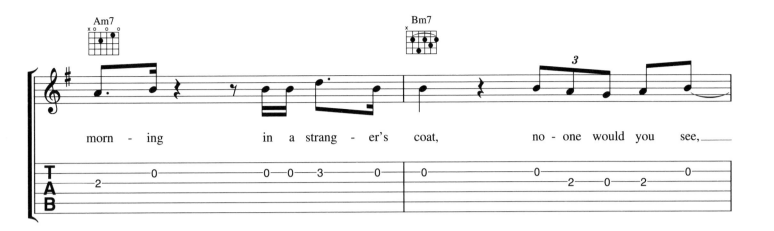

morn - ing   in a strang - er's coat,   no - one would you see,_____

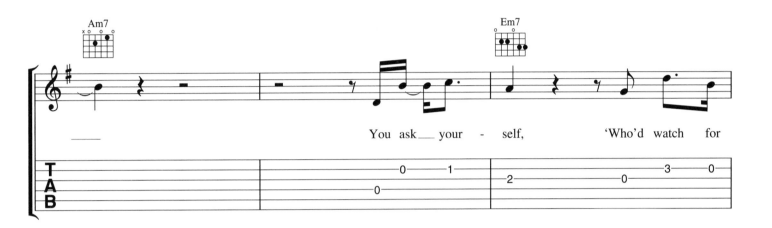

_____ You ask___ your - self,   'Who'd watch for

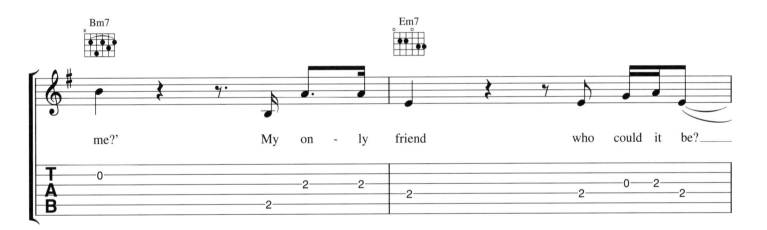

me?'   My on - ly friend   who could it be?_____

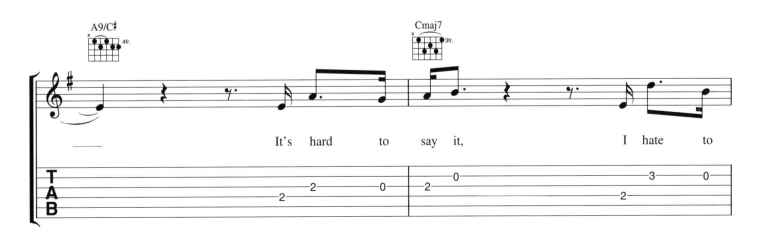

_____ It's hard to say it,   I hate to

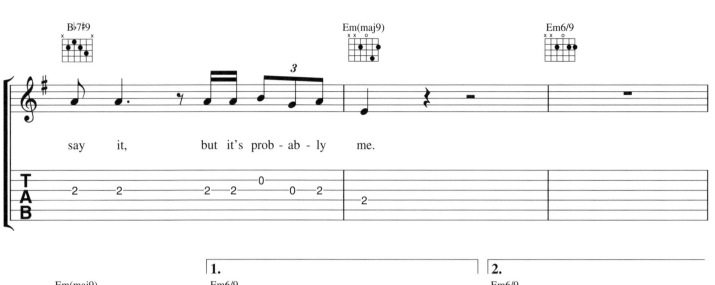

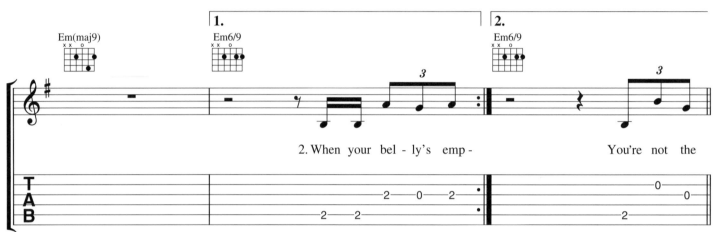

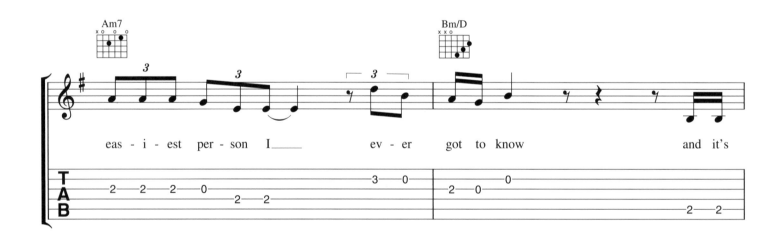

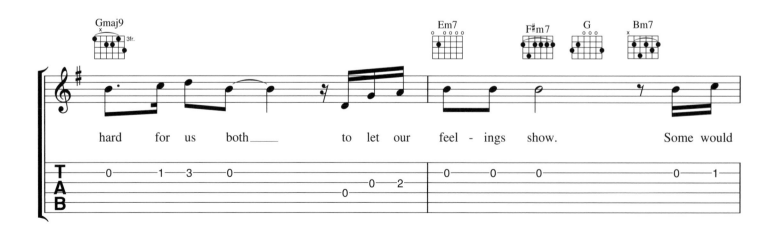

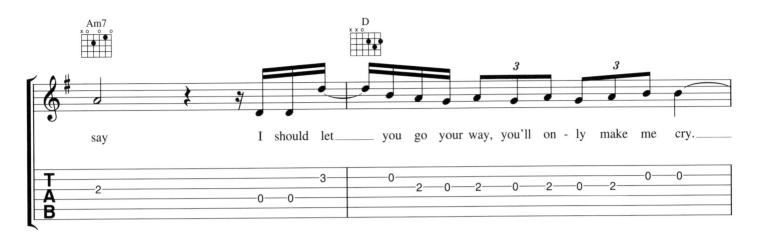

say   I should let_____ you go your way, you'll on - ly make me cry.

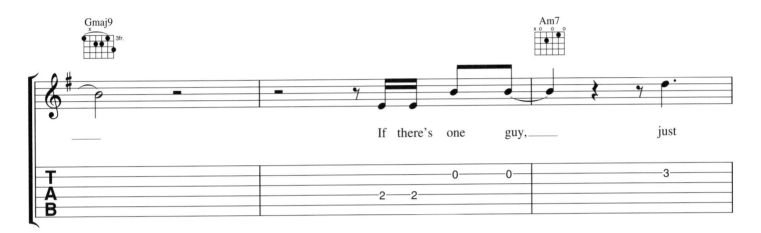

If there's one   guy,_____   just

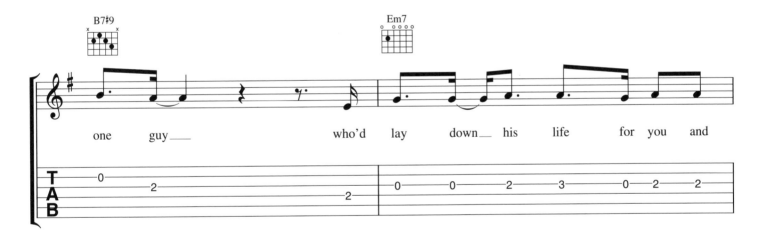

one guy____   who'd lay down___ his life for you and

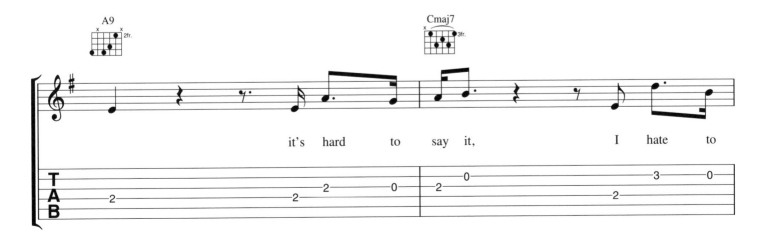

it's hard to say it,   I hate to

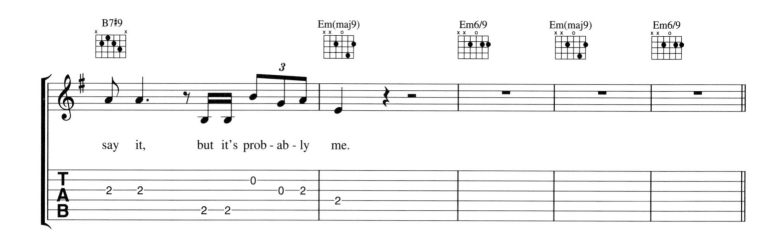

say it,   but it's prob - ab - ly   me.

Solo

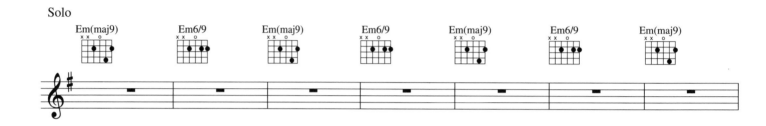

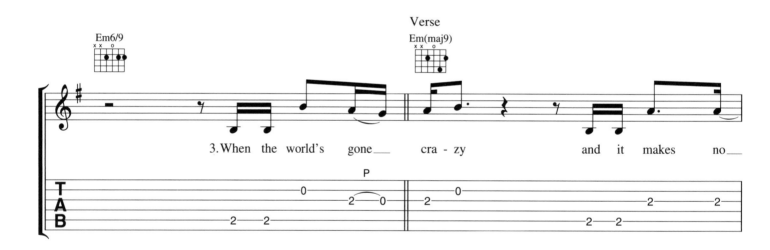

3. When the world's gone___ cra - zy and it makes no___

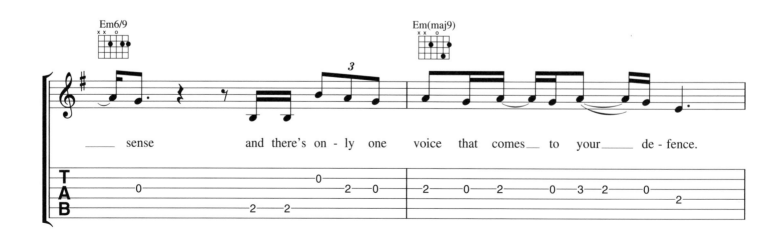

___ sense and there's on - ly one voice that comes___ to your___ de - fence.

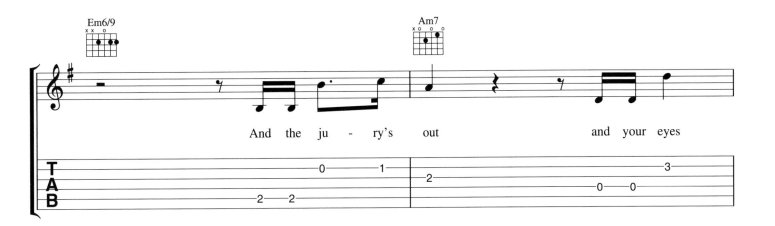

And the ju – ry's out and your eyes

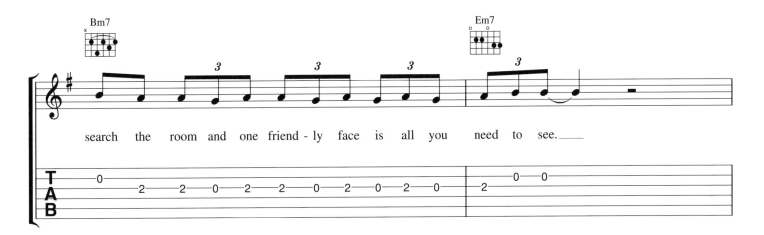

search the room and one friend - ly face is all you need to see.___

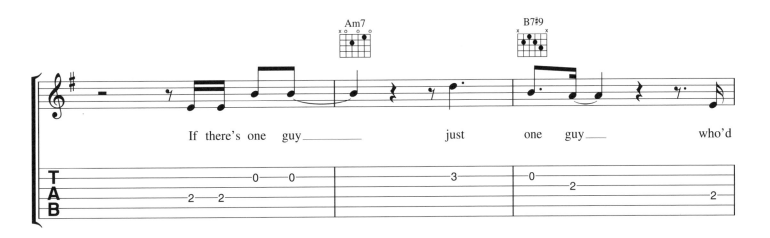

If there's one guy___ just one guy___ who'd

lay down___ his life for you and die, it's hard to

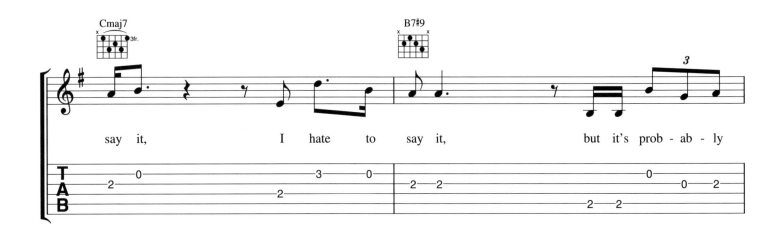

say it, I hate to say it, but it's prob-ab-ly

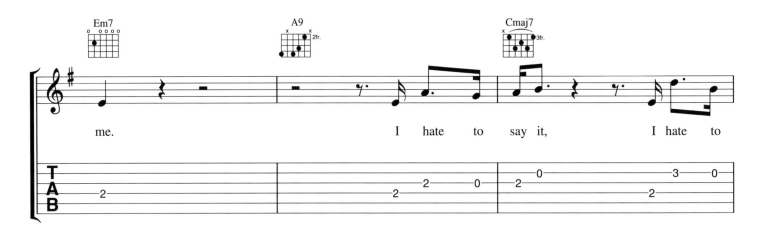

me. I hate to say it, I hate to

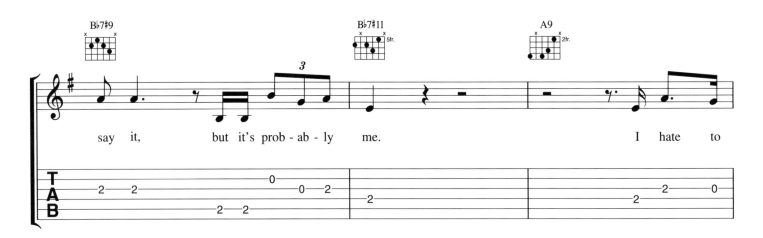

say it, but it's prob-ab-ly me. I hate to

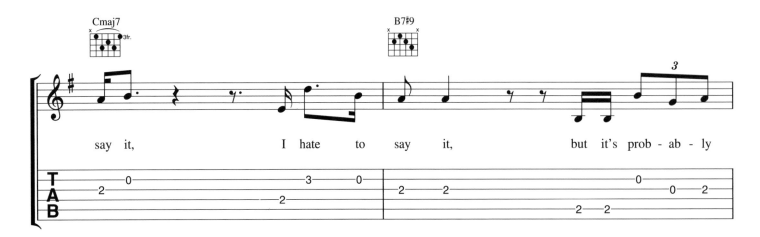

say it, I hate to say it, but it's prob-ab-ly

me.   I hate   to   say it,   I hate   to

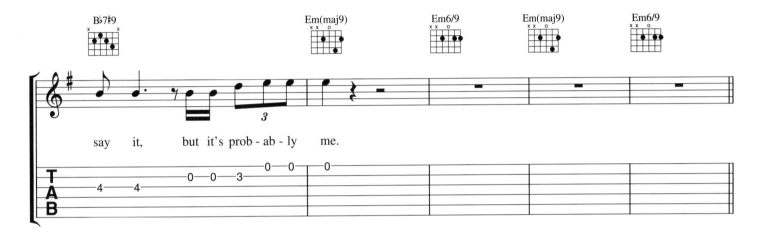

say   it,   but it's prob - ab - ly   me.

Instrumental Solo

Repeat to fade

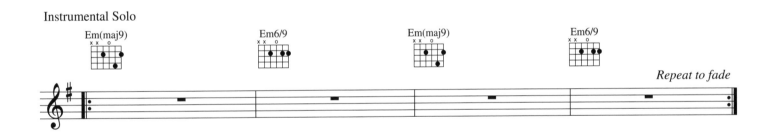

Verse 2   When your belly's empty
And the hunger's too real
And you're too proud to beg
And too dumb to steal,
You search the city for your only friend
No one would you see.
You ask yourself
Who could it be?
A solitary voice to speak out and set me free
I hate to say it, I hate to say it
But it's probably me.

Let Your Soul Be Your Pilot

Words & Music by Sting

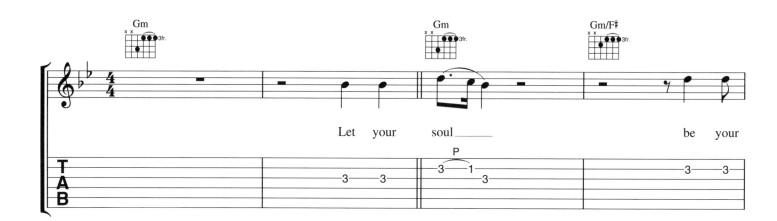

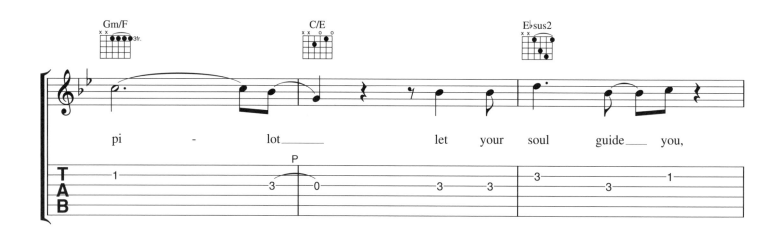

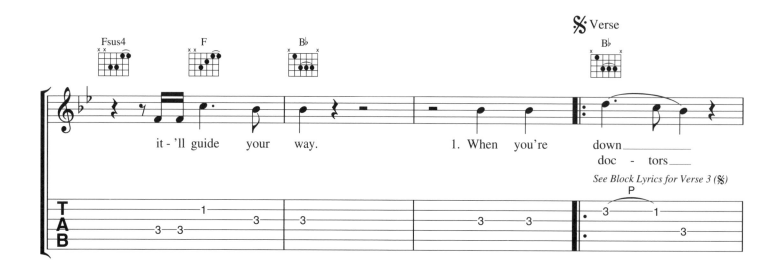

and they're count - ing,_____   when your se - cret's
fail to heal you,_____   when no medicine chest

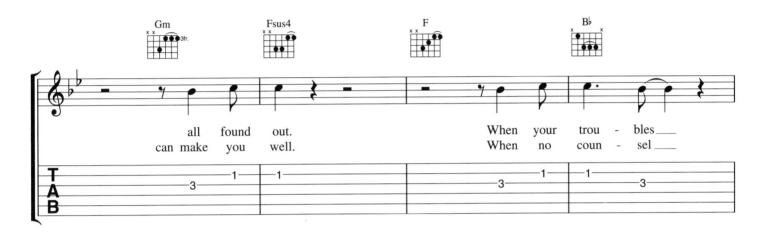

all found out.   When your trou - bles_____
can make you well.   When no coun - sel_____

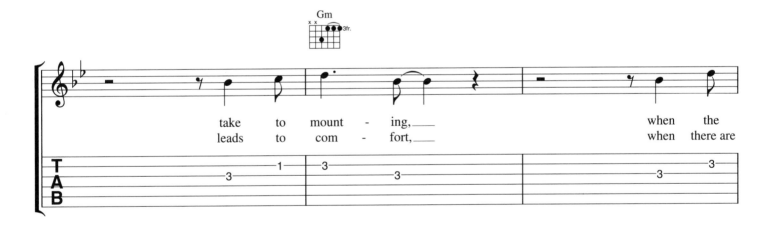

take to mount - ing,_____   when the
leads to com - fort,_____   when there are

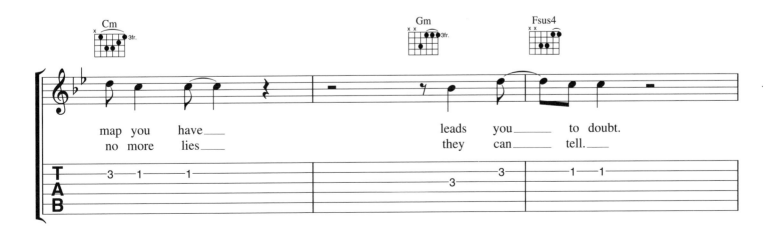

map you have_____   leads you_____ to doubt.
no more lies_____   they can_____ tell._____

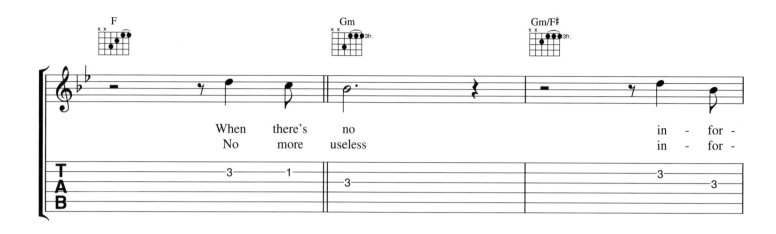

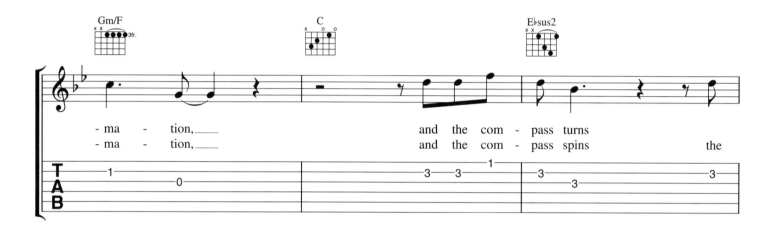

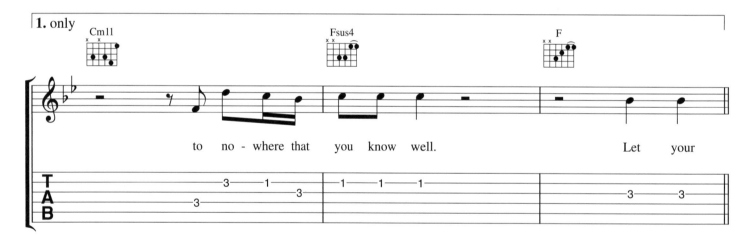

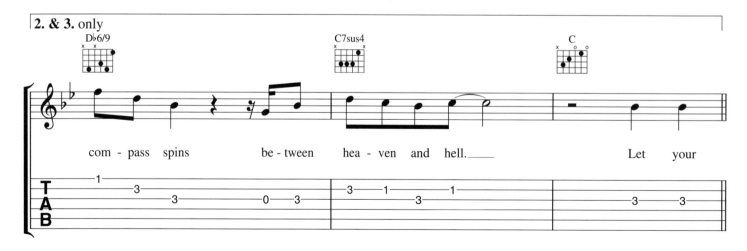

40

Chorus

B♭sus2 **B♭sus2/A♭** **G7sus4** **G7**

soul _____ be your pi - lot _____ let your

To Coda ⊕

E♭sus2 **Fsus4** **F** **B♭**

soul guide _____ you, he'll guide _____ you well.

1. | **2.** | **E♭sus2**

2. When the And your eyes turn to-ward _____ the win -

F **C7sus4** **B♭sus2/A♭**

- dow pane. To the lights _____ up - on the hill

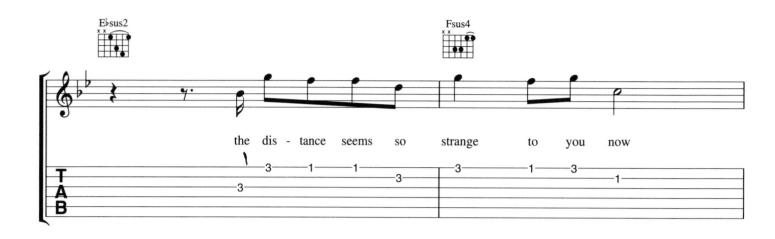

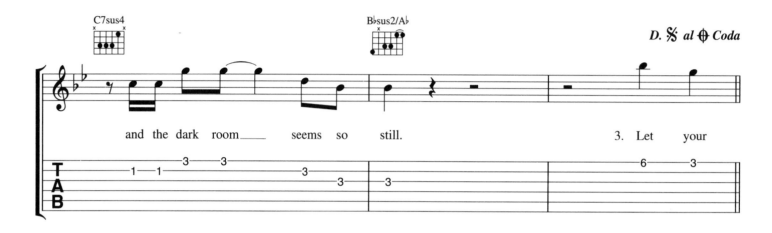

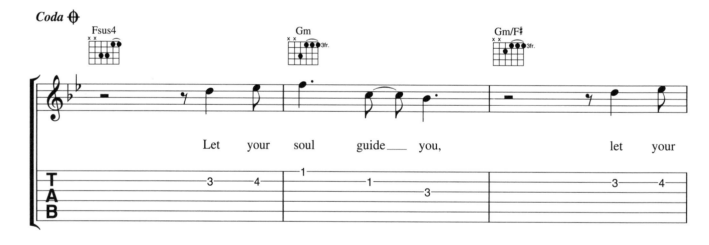

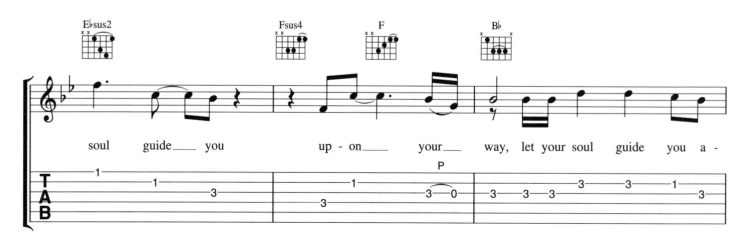

long the way, let your soul guide you a - long the way.

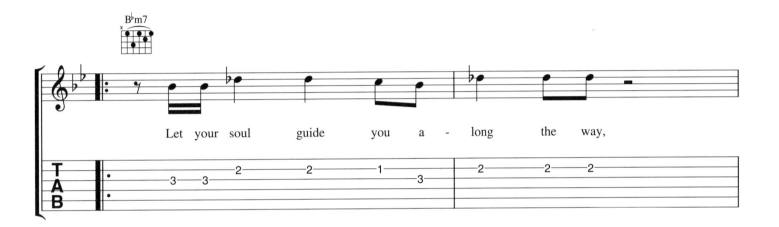

Let your soul guide you a - long the way,

Repeat ad lib to fade

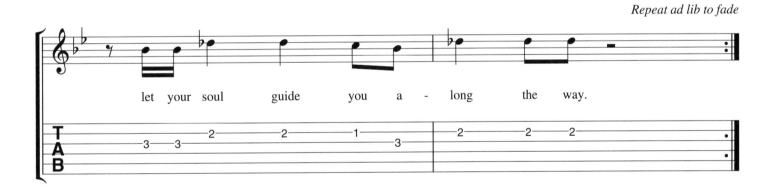

let your soul guide you a - long the way.

Verse 3 (%)   Let your pain be my sorrow
Let your tears be my tears too
Let your courage be my model
That the north you find will be true.
When there's no more information
And the compass turns
To nowhere, to nowhere that you know well.

Lithium Sunset

Words & Music by Sting

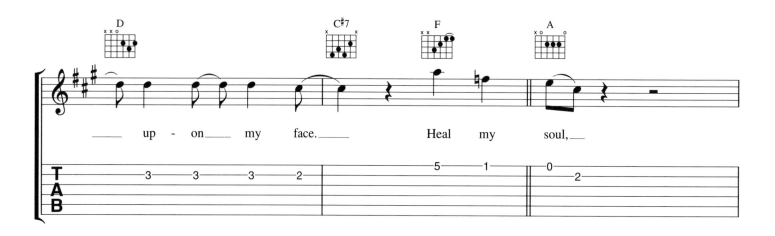

up - on my face. Heal my soul,

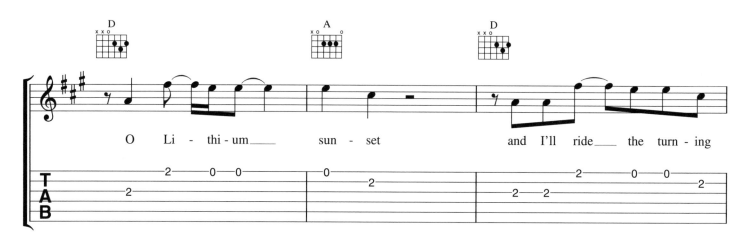

O Li - thi - um sun - set and I'll ride the turn - ing

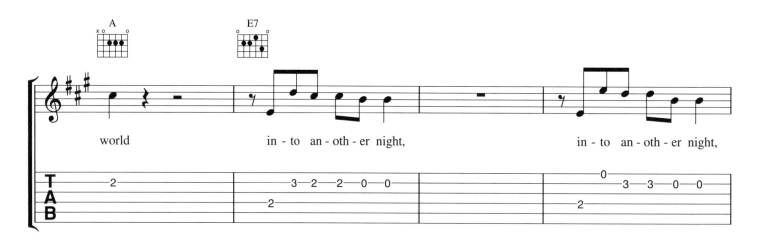

world in - to an - oth - er night, in - to an - oth - er night,

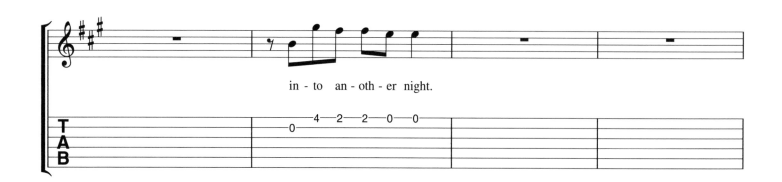

in - to an - oth - er night.

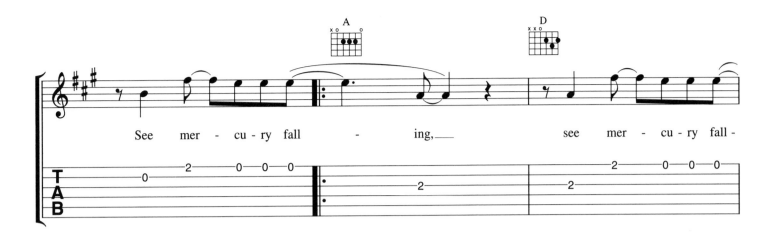

See mer - cu - ry fall - ing,___ see mer - cu - ry fall -

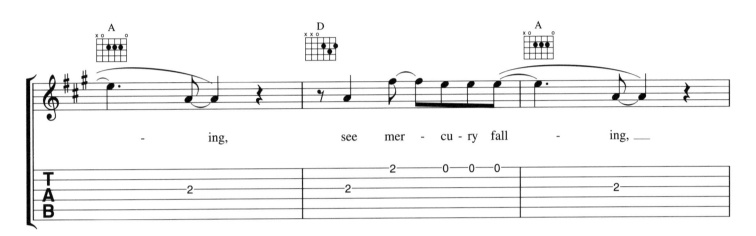

- ing, see mer - cu - ry fall - ing,___

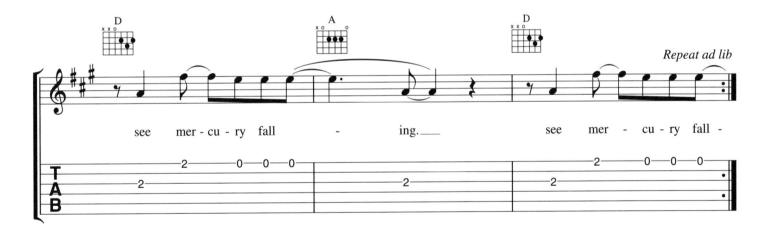

Repeat ad lib

see mer - cu - ry fall - ing.___ see mer - cu - ry fall -

Love Is The Seventh Wave

Words & Music by Sting

Verse

1. In the em - pire of the sens - es, you're the queen of all
2. Ev - 'ry rip - ple on the oc - ean, ev - 'ry leaf on ev -
3. Feel it ris - ing in the cit - ies, feel it sweep - ing ov -

See Block Lyrics for Verses 4&5

you sur - vey, all the cit - ies all the na - tions,
- 'ry tree, ev - 'ry sand dune in the des - ert,
- er land, ov - er bord - ers, ov - er front - iers,

Chorus

ev - 'ry - thing that falls your way. I say,
ev - 'ry power we nev - er see.
noth - ing will its power with - stand. I say,

There is a

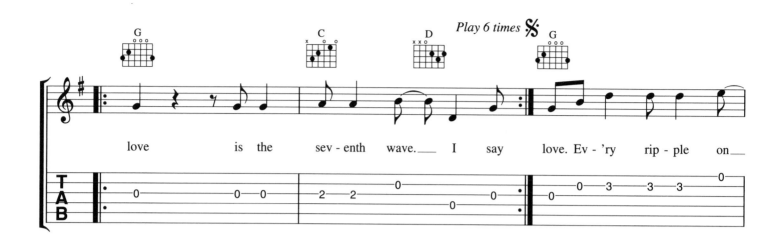

love   is the sev - enth wave.___ I say love. Ev - 'ry rip - ple on___

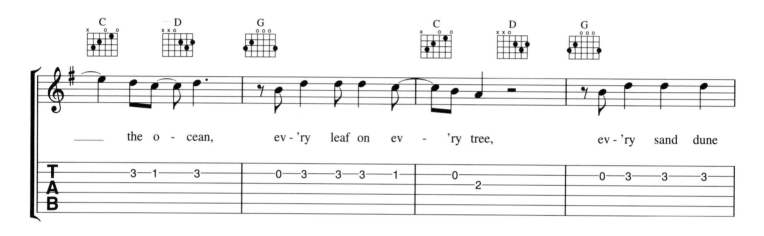

___ the o - cean, ev - 'ry leaf on ev - 'ry tree, ev - 'ry sand dune

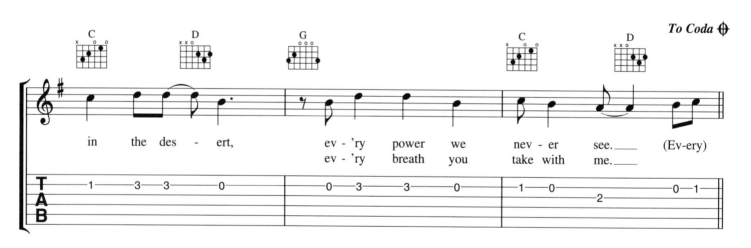

in the des - ert,   ev - 'ry power we nev - er see.___ (Ev-ery)
             ev - 'ry breath you take with me.___

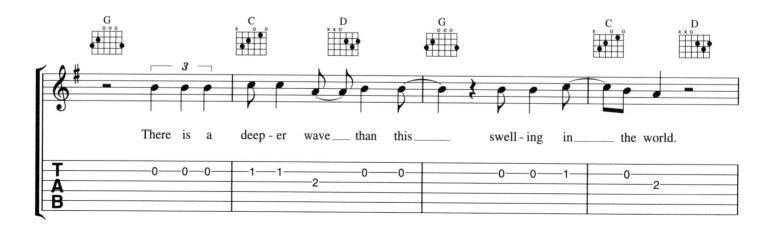

There is a deep - er wave___ than this_____ swell - ing in_____ the world.

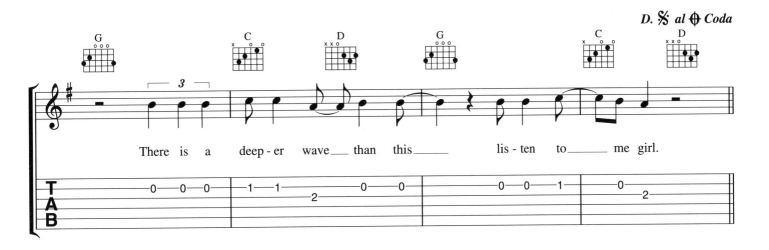

There is a deep-er wave___ than this_____ lis - ten to_____ me girl.

Coda ⊕

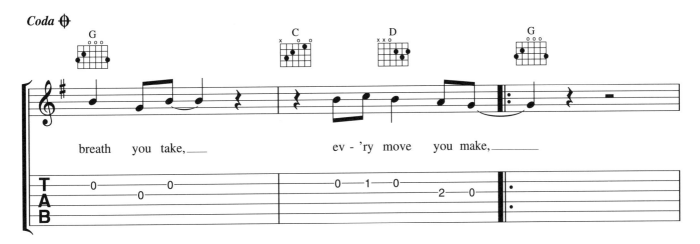

breath you take,___ ev - 'ry move you make,_____

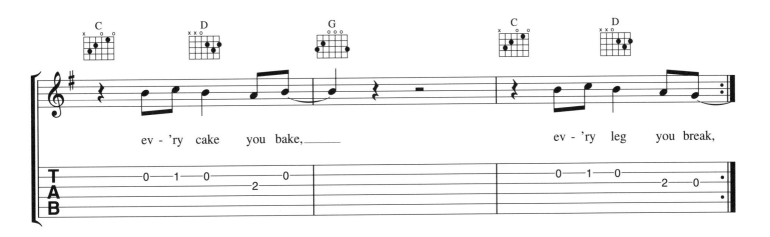

ev - 'ry cake you bake,_____ ev - 'ry leg you break,

Verse 4

All the bloodshed, all the anger
All the weapons all the greed
All the armies, all the missiles
All the symbols of your fear. I say
There is a deeper wave than this
Ringing in the world
There is a deeper wave than this
Listen to me, girl.

Verse 5

At the still point of destruction
At the centre of the fury
All the angels, all the devils
All around us, can't you see?
There is a deeper wave than this
Rising in the land
There is a deeper wave than this
Nothing will withstand.

If You Love Somebody Set Them Free

Words & Music by Sting

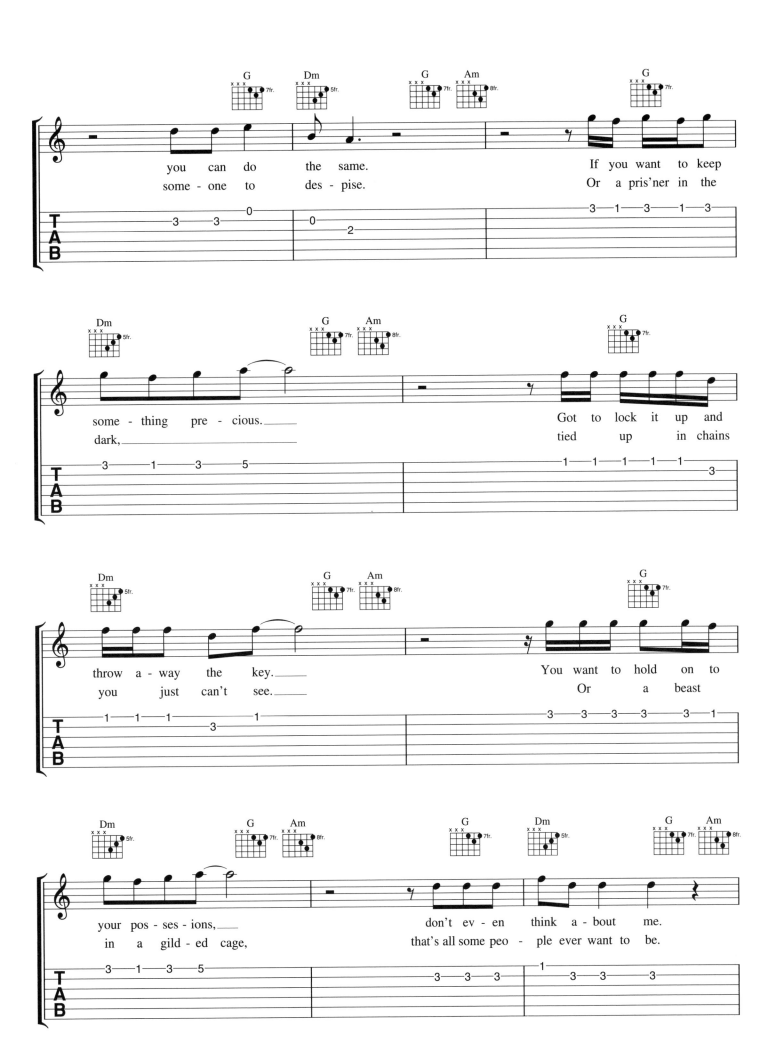

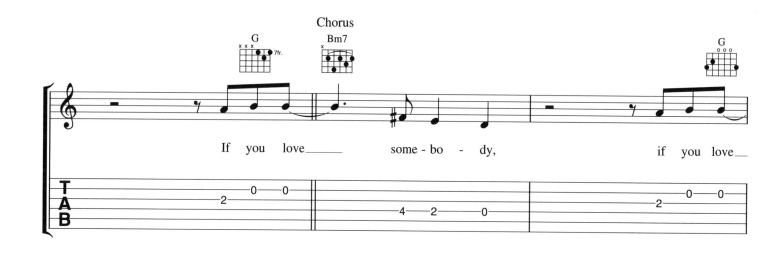

Chorus

If you love_____ some-bo - dy, if you love_____

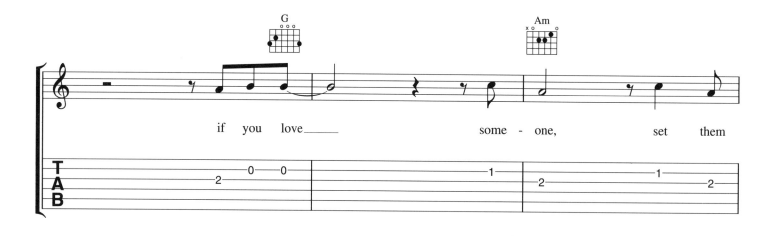

_____ some - one, if you love_____ some-bo - dy,

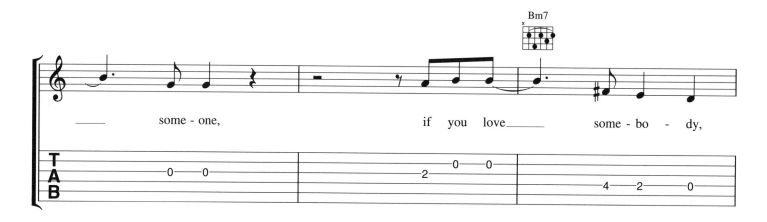

if you love_____ some - one, set them

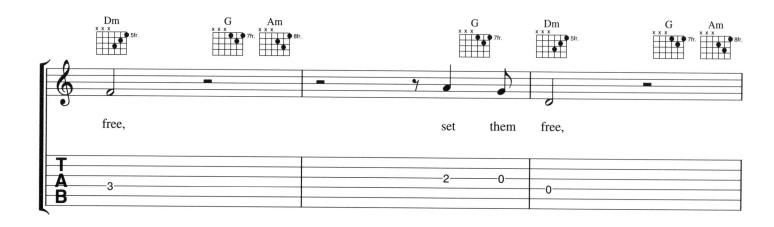

free, set them free,

Bridge

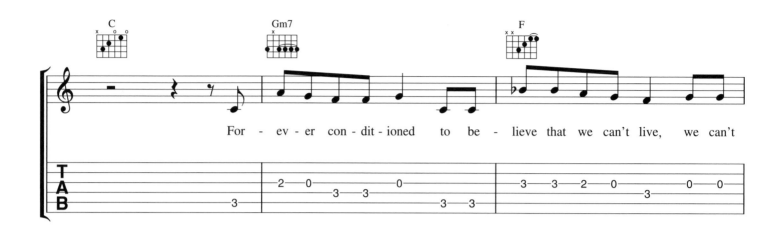

For - ev - er con - dit - ioned to be - lieve that we can't live, we can't

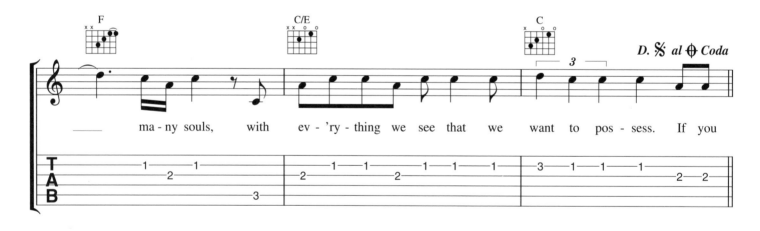

live here and be hap - py with less.___ With so man - y rich - es, so___

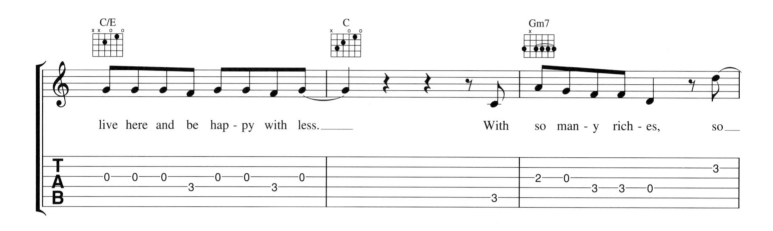

D. % al Coda

___ ma - ny souls, with ev - 'ry - thing we see that we want to pos - sess. If you

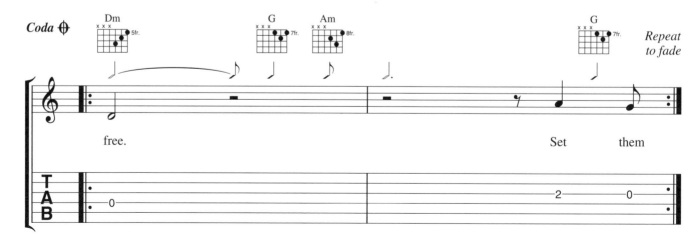

Coda

Repeat to fade

free.   Set   them

Message In A Bottle

Words & Music by Sting

1. Just a cast - a - way, an

See Block Lyrics for Verses 2 & 3 (%)

is - land lost at sea o, an - oth - er lone -

O. S. to the world, I'll send an S. O. S. to the world.

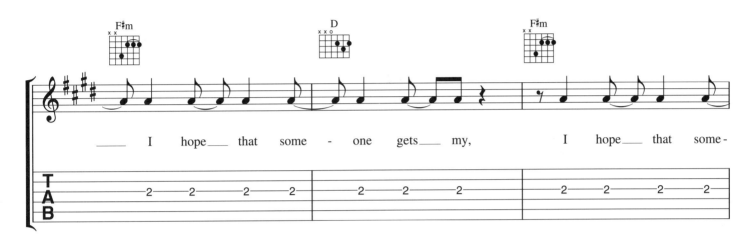

I hope that some - one gets my, I hope that some -

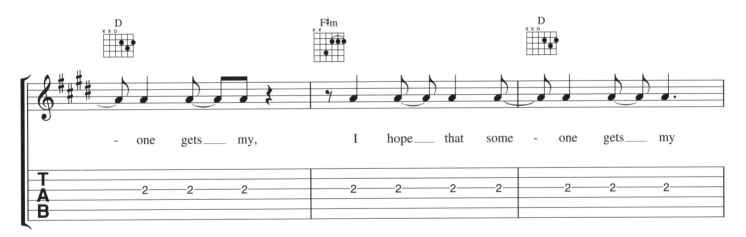

- one gets my, I hope that some - one gets my

To Coda ⊕

On 2nd chorus only
play 3 times

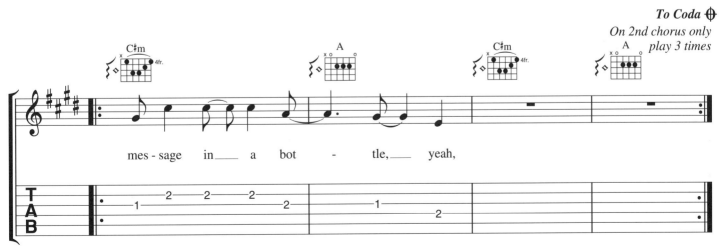

mes - sage in a bot - tle, yeah,

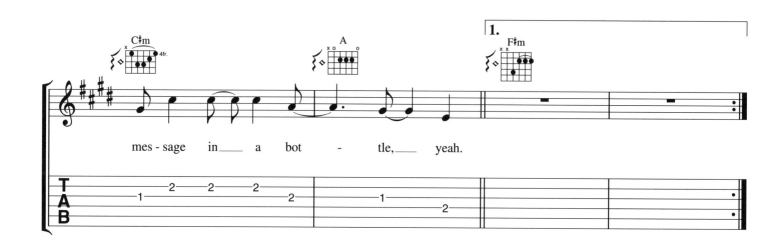

mes - sage in___ a bot - tle,___ yeah.

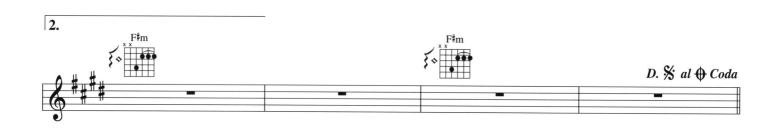

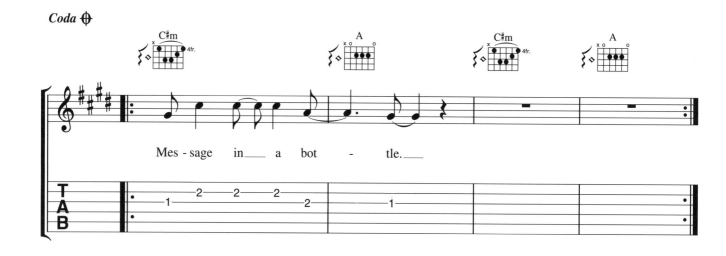

Coda ⊕

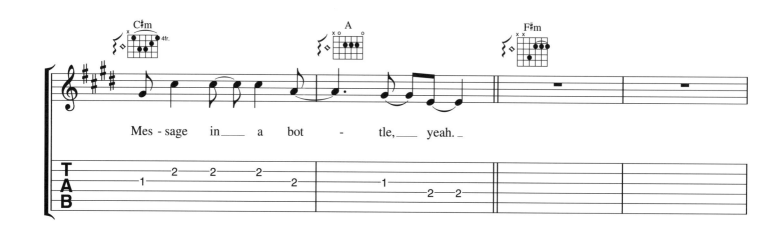

Mes - sage in___ a bot - tle.___

Mes - sage in___ a bot - tle,___ yeah.___

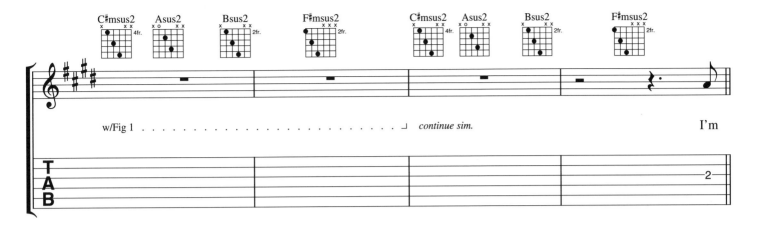

w/Fig 1 . . . . ⌐ *continue sim.*

I'm

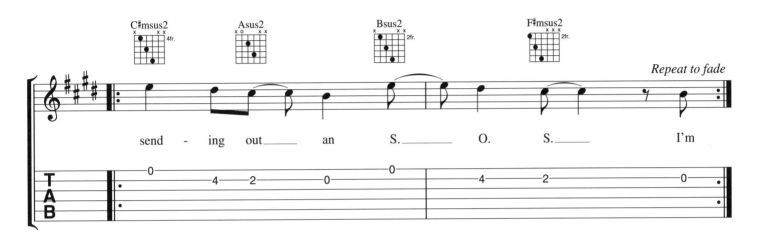

Repeat to fade

send - ing out___ an S.___ O. S.___ I'm

Verse 2   A year has passed since I wrote my note
But I should have known this right from the start
Only hope can keep me together
Love can mend your life but love can break your heart.

Verse 3(𝄋)   Walked out this morning, I don't believe what I saw
A hundred billion bottles washed up on the shore
Seems like I'm not alone in being alone
Hundred billion cast aways looking for a home.

Roxanne

Words & Music by Sting

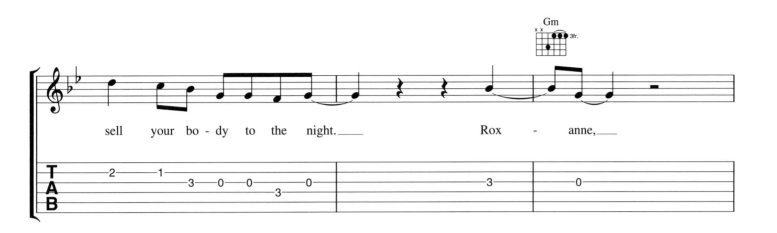

sell   your   bo - dy   to   the   night.___   Rox - anne,___

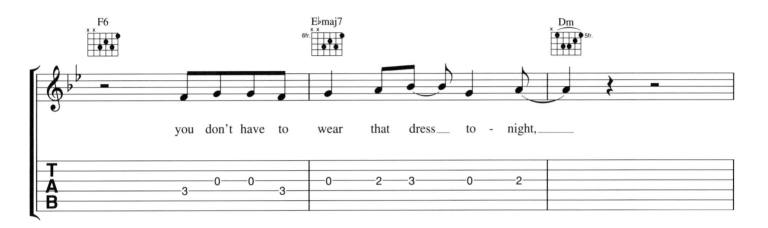

you   don't   have   to   wear   that   dress___   to - night,___

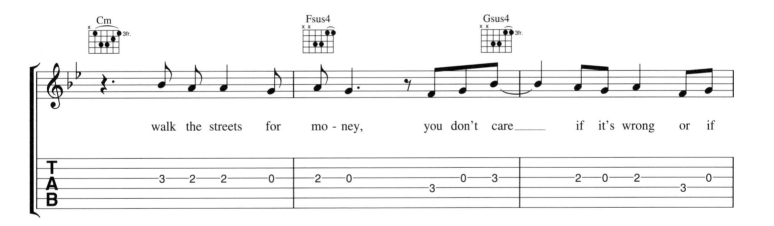

walk   the   streets   for   mo - ney,   you   don't   care___   if   it's   wrong   or   if

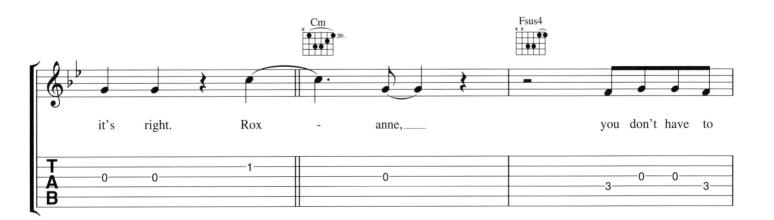

it's   right.   Rox - anne,___   you   don't   have   to

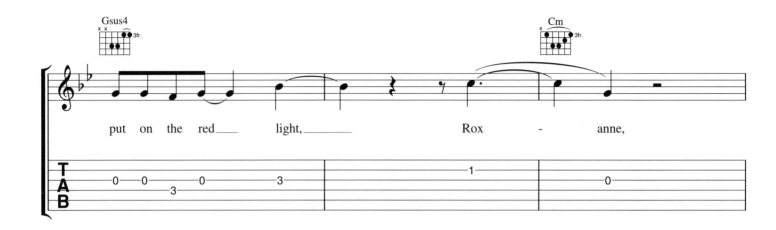

put on the red___ light,_____ Rox - anne,

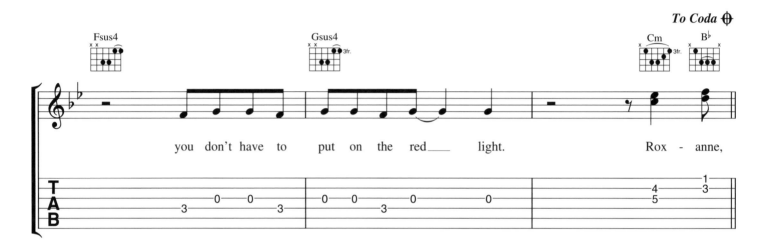

To Coda ⊕

you don't have to put on the red___ light. Rox - anne,

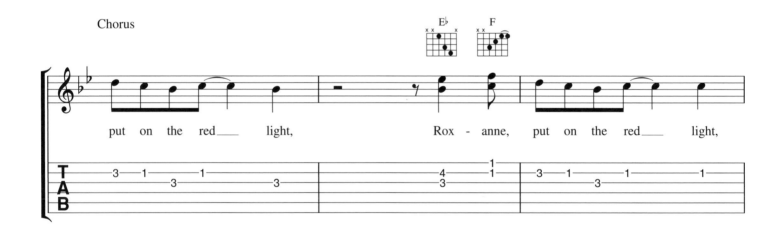

Chorus

put on the red___ light, Rox - anne, put on the red___ light,

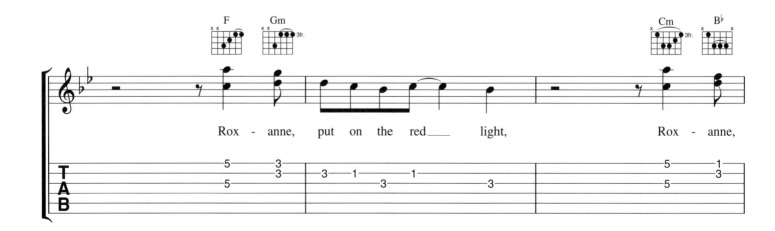

Rox - anne, put on the red___ light, Rox - anne,

Verse 2(%)   I loved you since I knew ya
I wouldn't talk down to ya
I have to tell you just how I feel
I won't share you with another boy.
I know my mind is made up
Told you once, I won't tell you again,
It's a bad way.

She's Too Good For Me

Words & Music by Sting

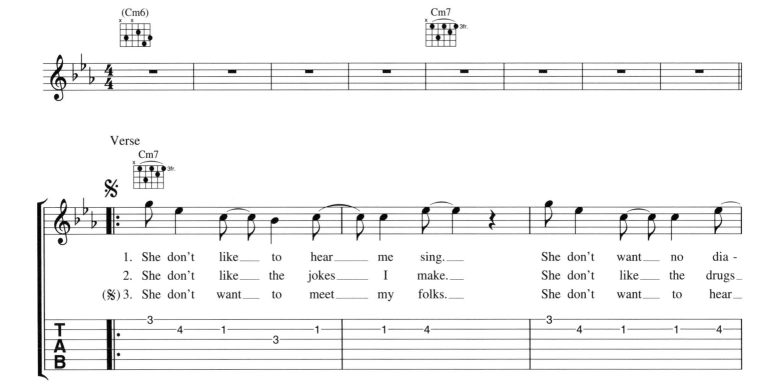

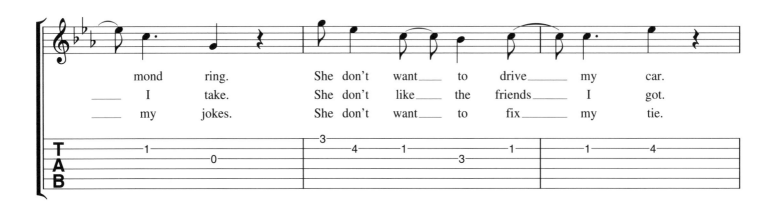

She won't let___ me go_____ that far. She don't like___ the way___
She don't like___ my friends_____ a lot. She don't like___ the clothes_
She don't ev - en want_____ to try. She don't like___ the books_

___ I look. She don't like___ the things___ I cook.
___ I wear. She don't like___ the way___ I stare.
___ I read. She don't like___ the way___ I feel.

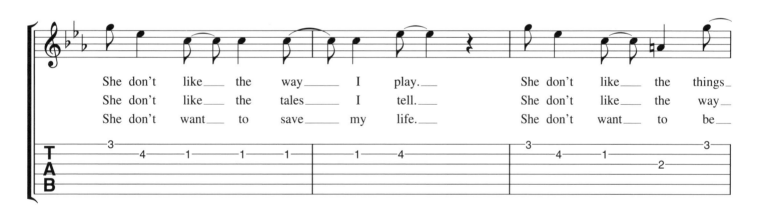

She don't like___ the way___ I play.___ She don't like___ the things_
She don't like___ the tales___ I tell.___ She don't like___ the way_
She don't want___ to save___ my life.___ She don't want___ to be___

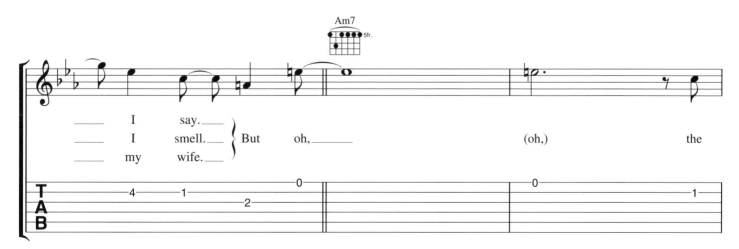

___ I say.___ But oh,_____ (oh,) the
___ I smell.___ my wife.___

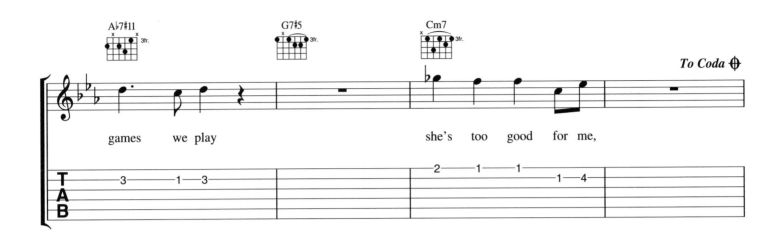

games   we play   she's   too   good   for me,

To Coda ⊕

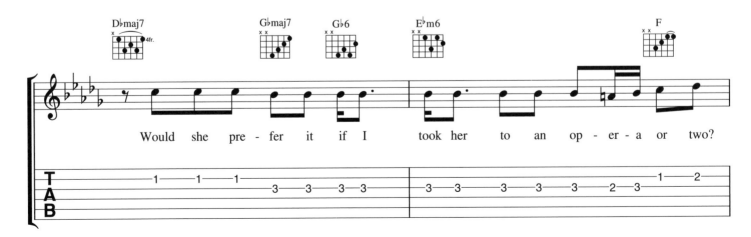

1. N.C.   **2.** N.C.

she's   too   good   for   me.

Half time ♪ = ♩

Gm/B♭   A7   E♭7   D7sus   D7

Would   she   pre - fer   it   if   I   washed   my - self   more   of - ten   than   I   do?

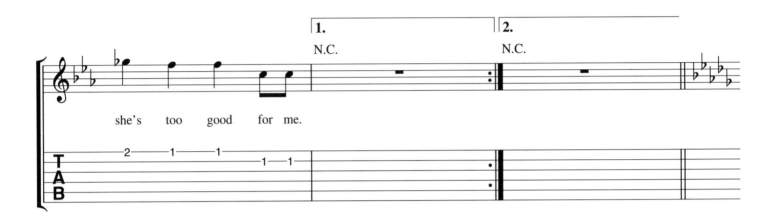

D♭maj7   G♭maj7   G♭6   E♭m6   F

Would   she   pre - fer   it   if   I   took   her   to   an   op - er - a   or   two?

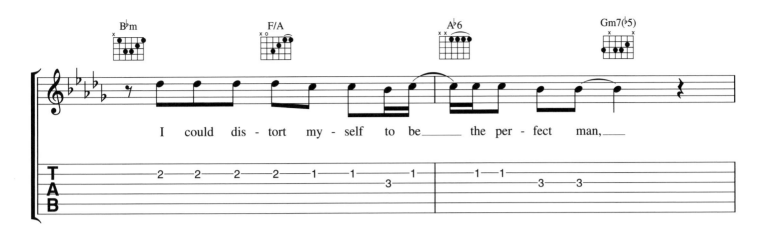

I could dis - tort my - self to be_____ the per - fect man,_____

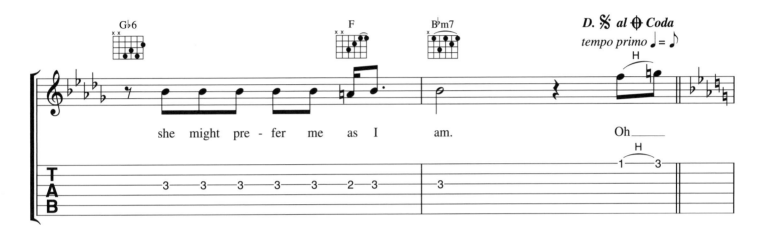

she might pre - fer me as I am. Oh_____

D. % al Coda
tempo primo

Coda

She's   too   good   for   me

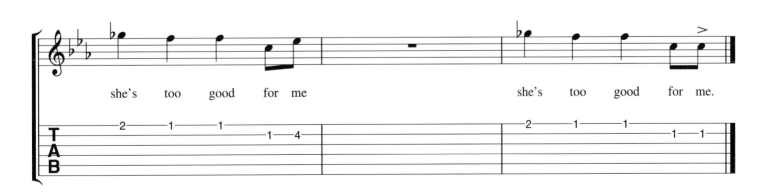

she's   too   good   for   me   she's   too   good   for   me.

So Lonely

Words & Music by Sting

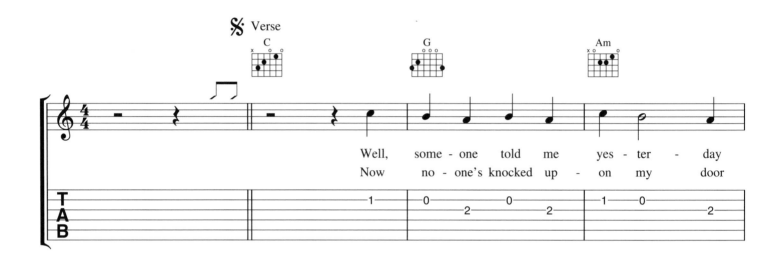

Well, some-one told me yes-ter-day
Now no-one's knocked up-on my door

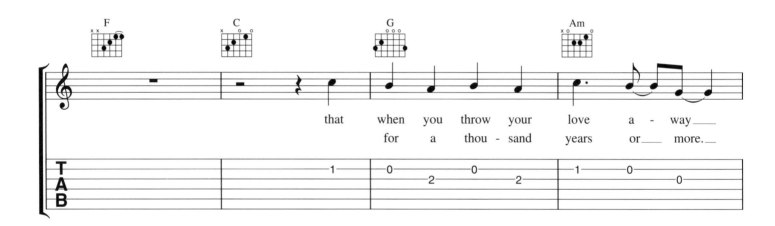

that when you throw your love a - way
for a thou - sand years or more.

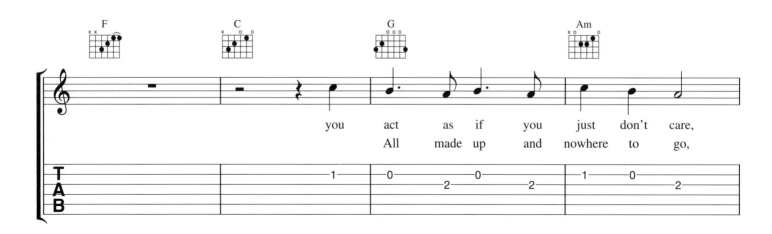

you act as if you just don't care,
All made up and nowhere to go,

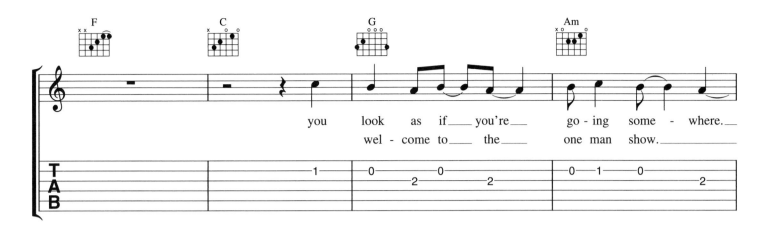

you look as if___ you're___ go - ing some - where.___
wel - come to___ the___ one man show._____

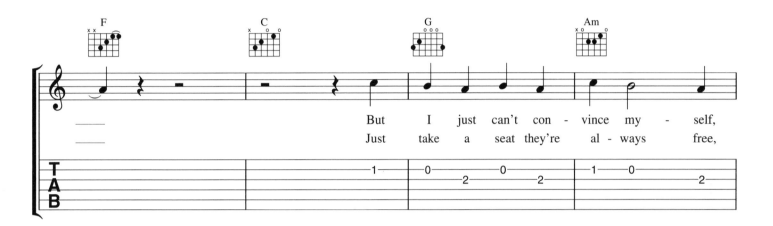

___ But I just can't con - vince my - self,
___ Just take a seat they're al - ways free,

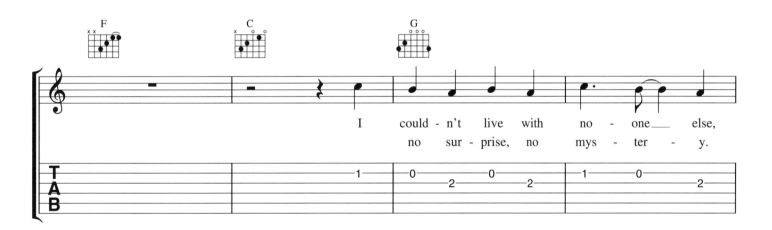

I could - n't live with no - one___ else,
no sur - prise, no mys - ter - y.

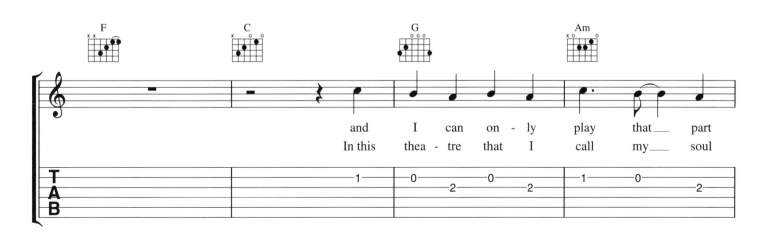

and I can on - ly play that___ part
In this thea - tre that I call my___ soul

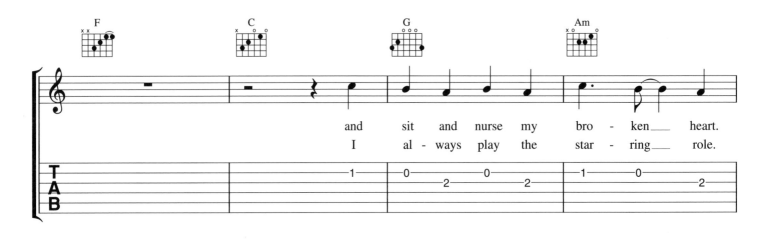

and   sit   and nurse   my   bro - ken___   heart.
I   al - ways   play   the   star - ring___   role.

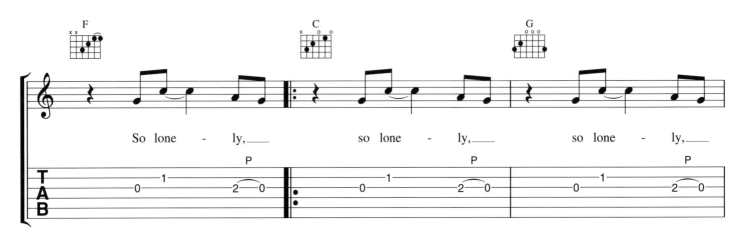

So lone - ly,___   so lone - ly,___   so lone - ly,___

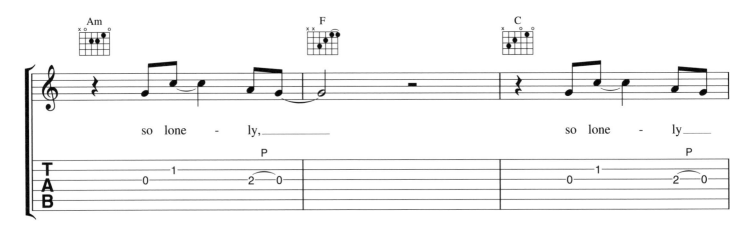

so lone - ly,_____   so lone - ly___

1.

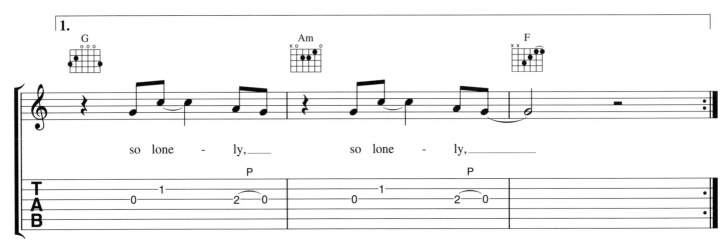

so lone - ly,___   so lone - ly,_____

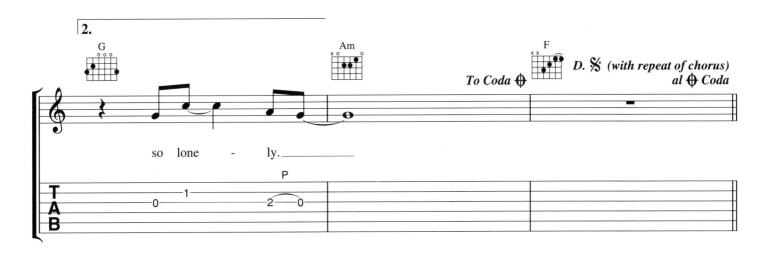

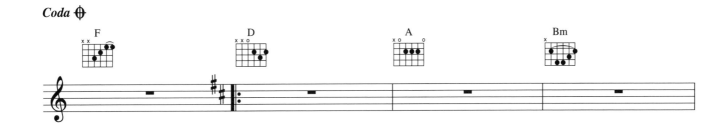

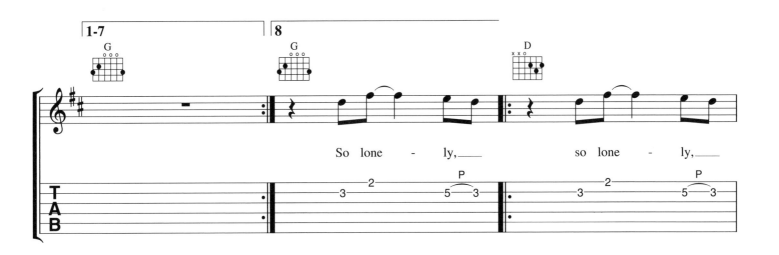

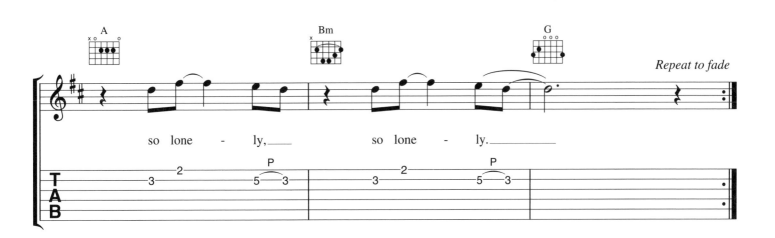

The Hounds Of Winter

Words & Music by Sting

dark as De-cem-ber, I'm as cold_____ as the man in the moon.

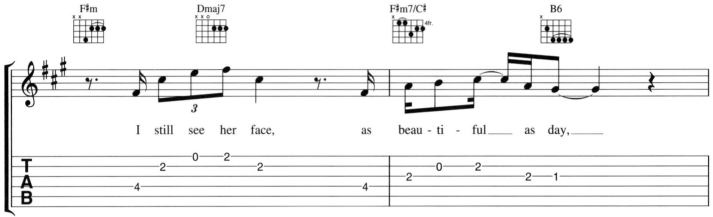

I still see her face, as beau-ti-ful_____ as day,_____

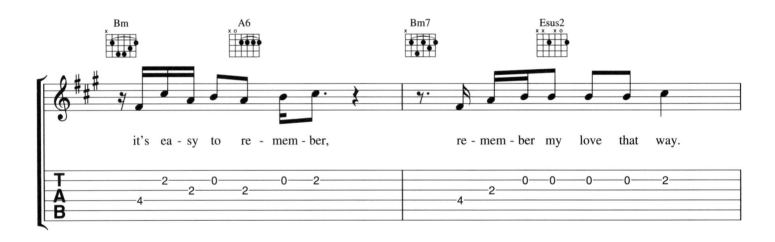

it's ea-sy to re-mem-ber, re-mem-ber my love that way.

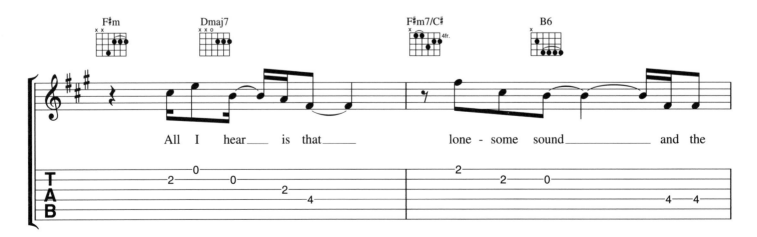

All I hear____ is that____ lone-some sound_____ and the

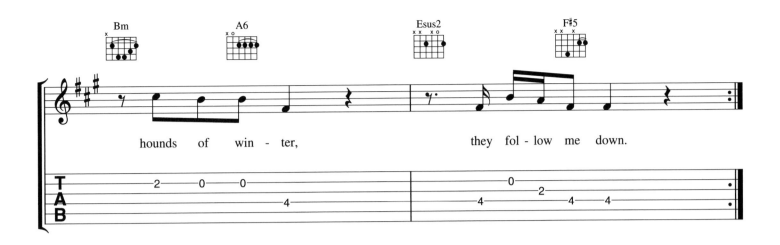

hounds   of   win - ter,   they fol - low me down.

To Coda ✛
D. 𝄋 al ✛ *Coda*

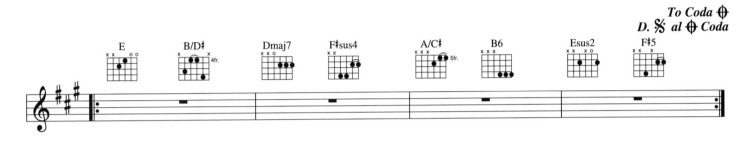

Coda ✛

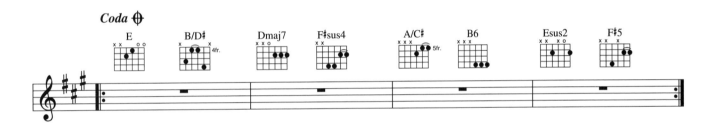

Repeat to fade

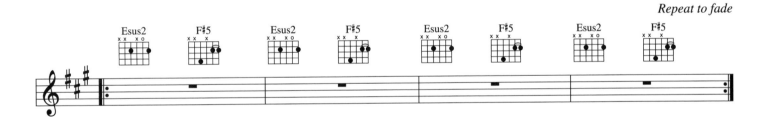

Verse 3

I can't make up the fire
The way that she could
I spend all my days
In the search for dry wood
Board all the windows
And close the front door
I can't believe
She won't go home any more.

Verse 4 (𝄋)

A season for joy
A season for sorrow
Where she's gone
I will surely, surely follow
She brightened my day
She warmed the coldest night
The hounds of winter
They got me in their sights.

Walking On The Moon

Words & Music by Sting

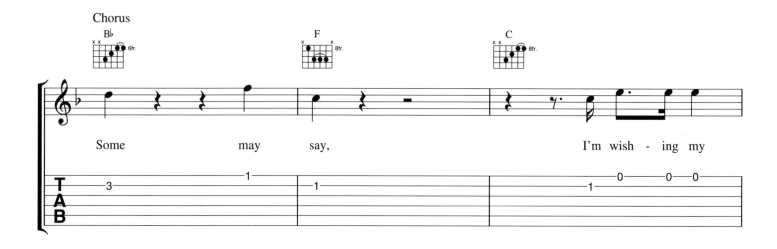

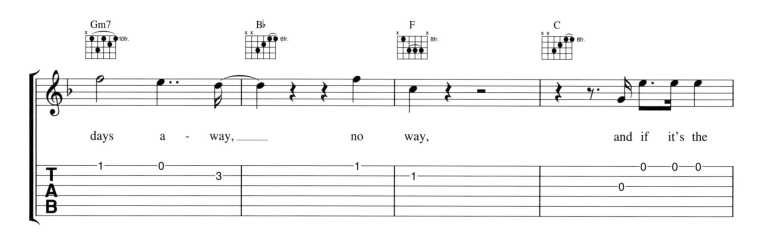

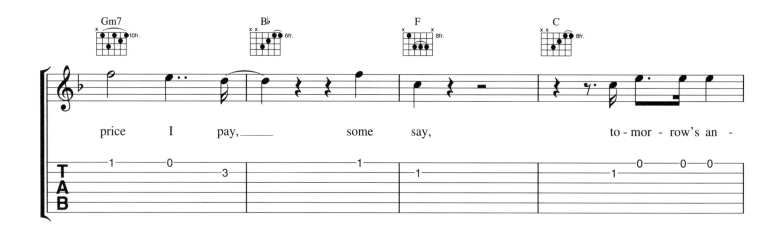

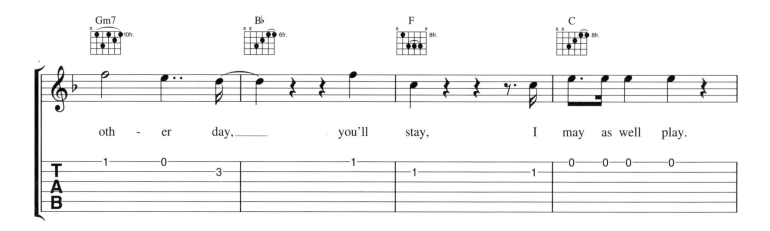

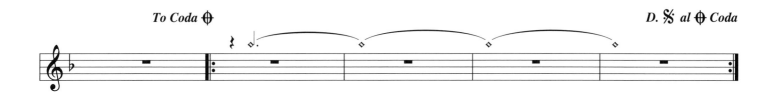

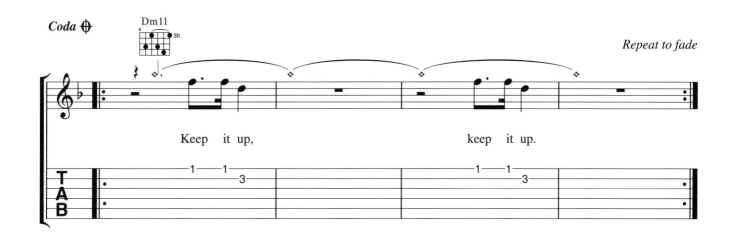

Keep   it up,   keep   it up.

We'll Be Together

Words & Music by Sting

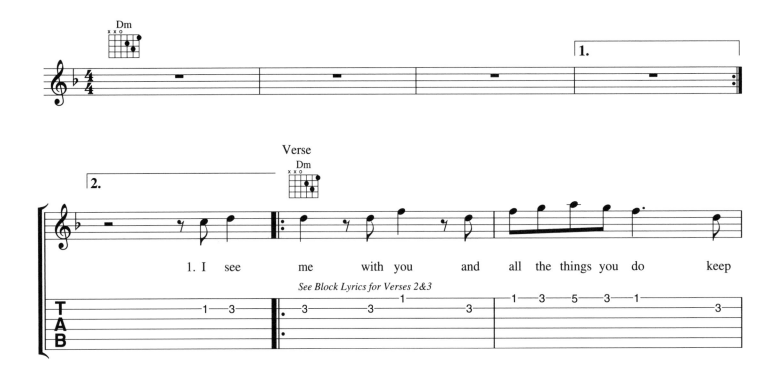

See Block Lyrics for Verses 2&3

1. I see me with you and all the things you do keep

turn - ing round and round in my mind.___ For - get the wea - ther, we should

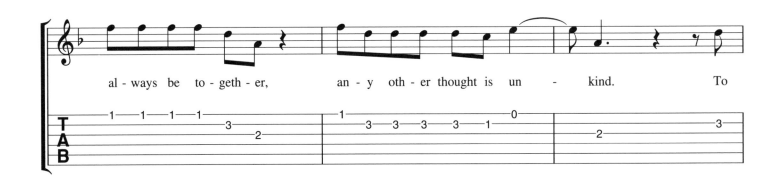

al - ways be to - geth - er, an - y oth - er thought is un - kind. To

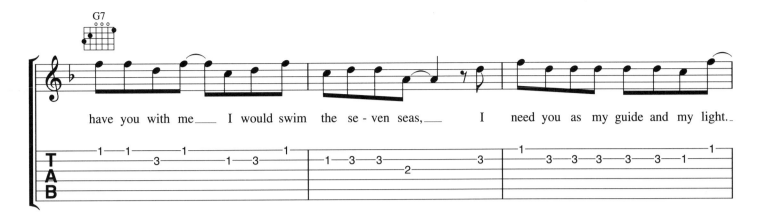

have you with me____ I would swim the se - ven seas,____ I need you as my guide and my light.____

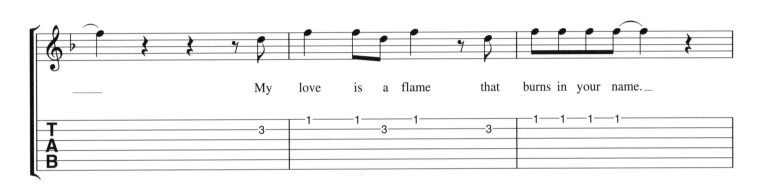

____ My love is a flame that burns in your name.____

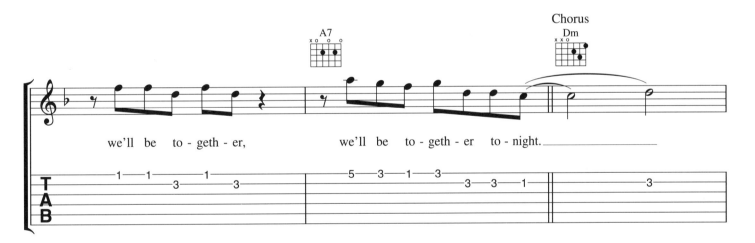

we'll be to - geth - er, we'll be to - geth - er to - night.____

Chorus

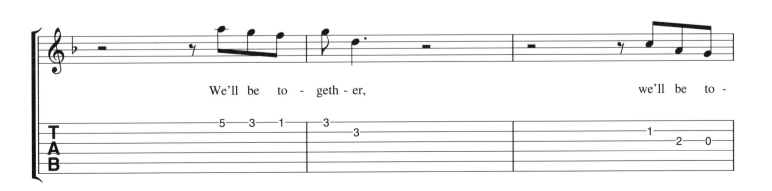

We'll be to - geth - er, we'll be to -

geth - er,   we'll be to - geth - er.

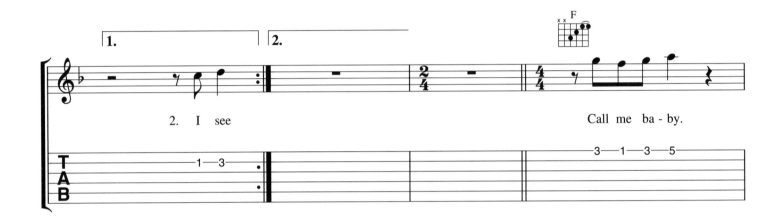

1. **2.**

2. I see   Call me ba - by.

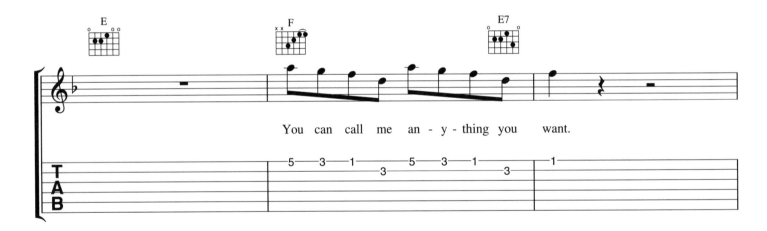

You can call me an - y - thing you   want.

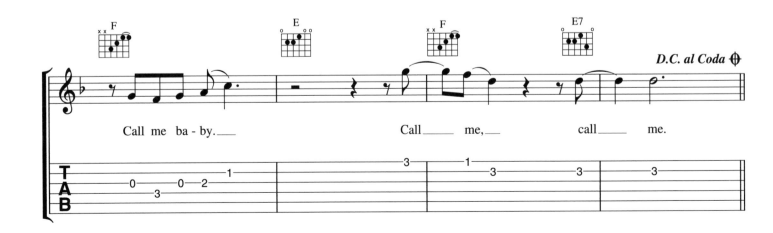

D.C. al Coda ⊕

Call me ba - by.___   Call___ me,___   call___ me.

Coda

We'll_____ be to - geth - er, we'll be to - geth - er to - night.___

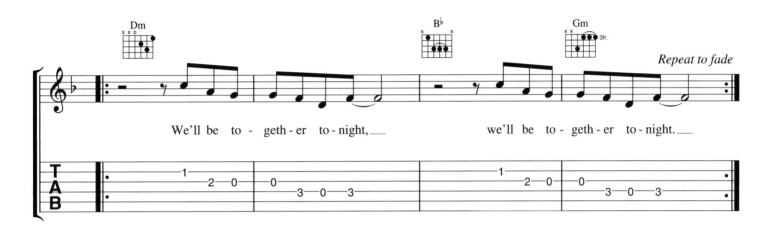

Repeat to fade

We'll be to - geth - er to - night,___ we'll be to - geth - er - to - night.___

Verse 2	I see you with me
	And all I want to be
	Is dancing here with you in my arms.
	Forget the weather,
	We should always be together,
	I'll always be a slave to your charms.
	To have you with me I would swim the seven seas;
	I need you as my guide and my light.
	My love is a flame that burns in your name,
	We'll be together tonight.

Verse 3	I see you with me
	And baby makes three.
	I see me with you,
	All the things we do.
	Forget the weather,
	We should always be together,
	I need you as my guide and my light.
	My love is a flame that burns in your name,
	We'll be together, we'll be together tonight.

Wrapped Around Your Finger

Words & Music by Sting

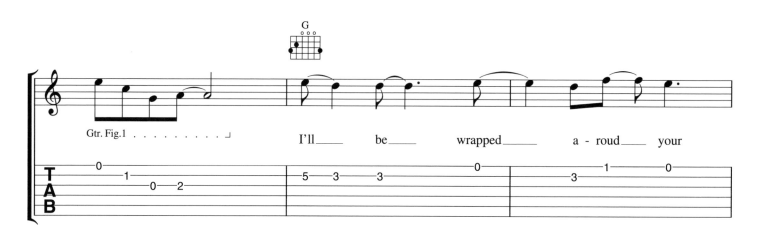

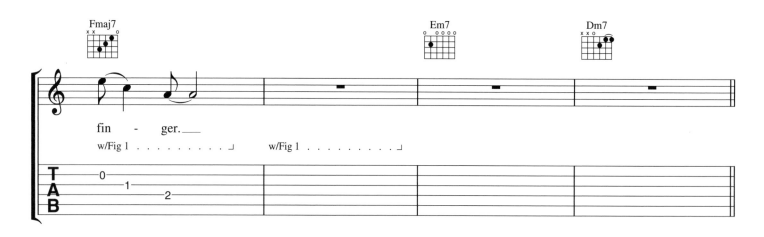

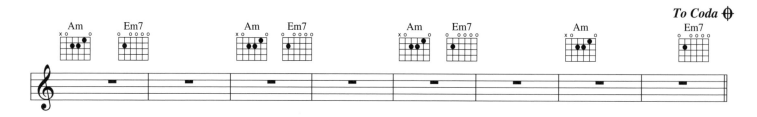

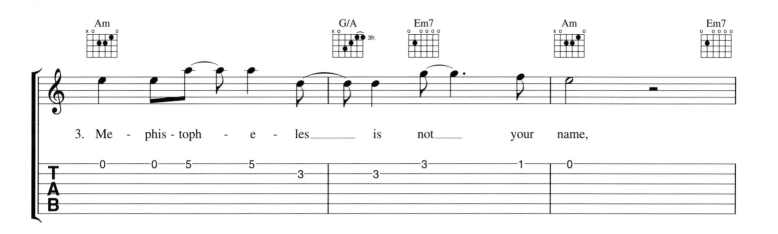

3. Me - phis - toph - e - les_____ is not_____ your name,

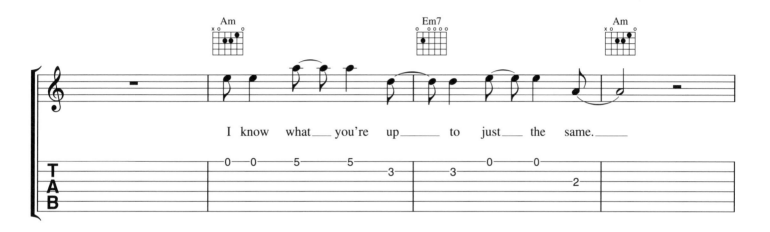

I know what___ you're up ___ to just___ the same._____

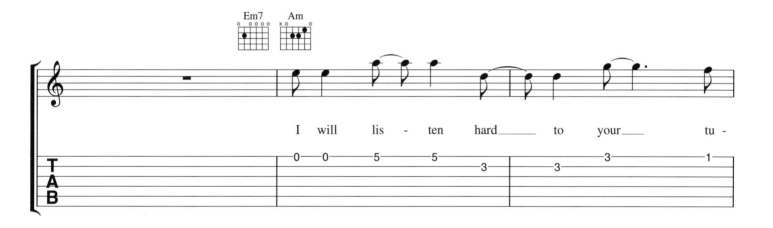

I will lis - ten hard_____ to your___ tu -

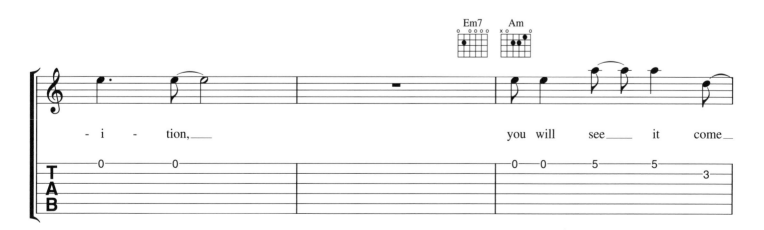

- i - tion,___ you will see___ it come___

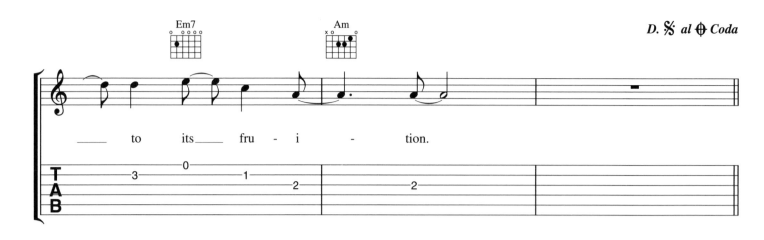

_____ to   its _____ fru - i -   tion.

Coda ⊕

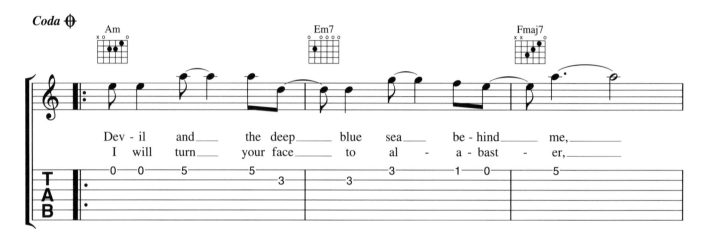

Dev - il   and _____ the deep _____ blue   sea _____ be - hind _____ me,
I   will   turn _____ your face _____ to   al - a - bast -   er, _____

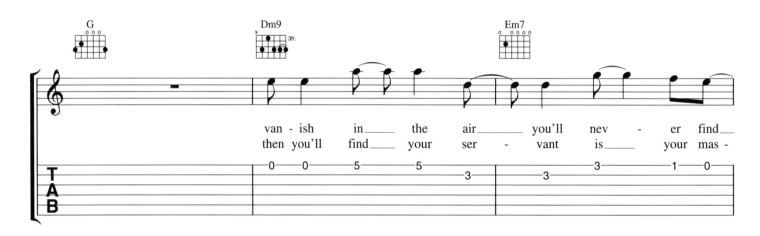

van - ish   in _____ the   air _____ you'll nev - er find
then you'll find _____ your ser - vant is _____ your mas -

1.

2.

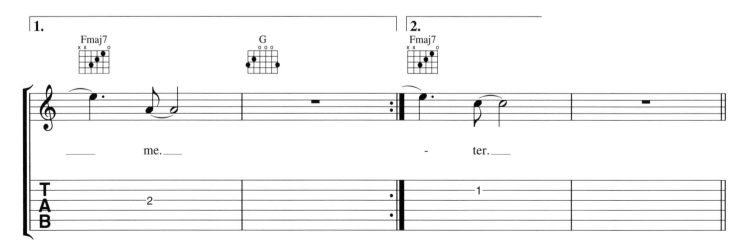

_____   me. _____   - ter. _____

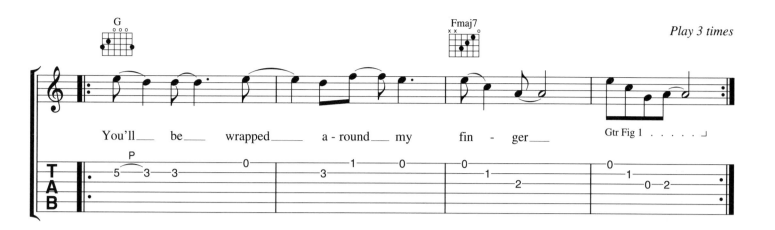

Play 3 times

You'll___ be___ wrapped_____ a - round___ my   fin - ger___

Gtr Fig 1 . . . . . .⌐

Repeat to fade

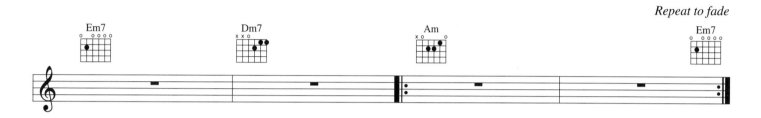

Valparaiso

Words & Music by Sting

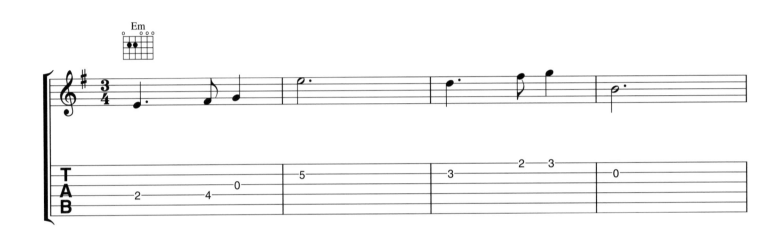

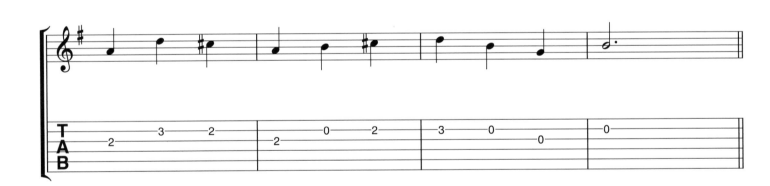

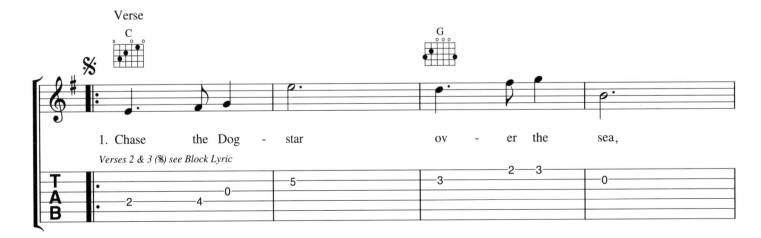

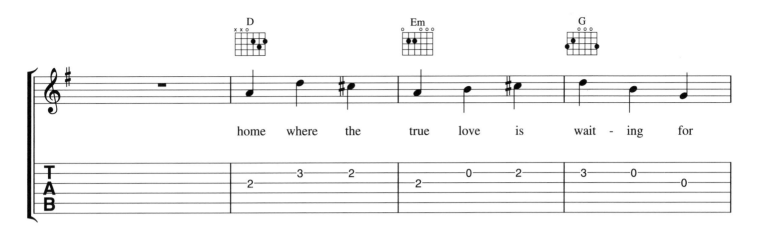

home where the true love is wait - ing for

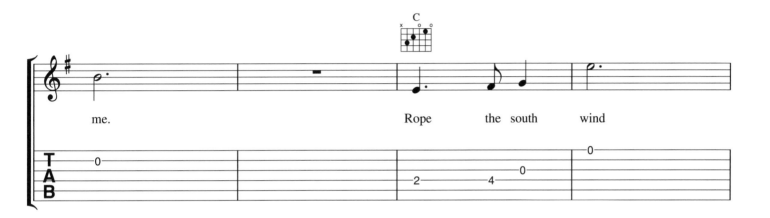

me. Rope the south wind

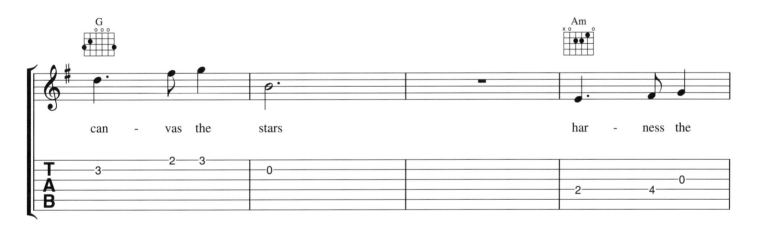

can - vas the stars har - ness the

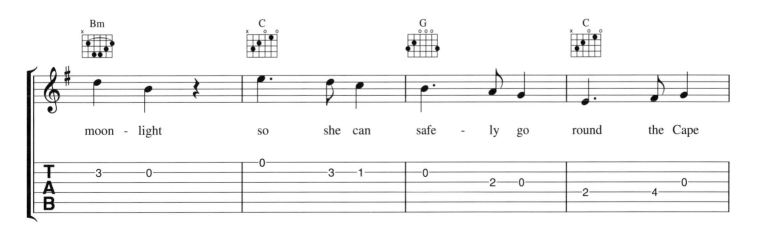

moon - light so she can safe - ly go round the Cape

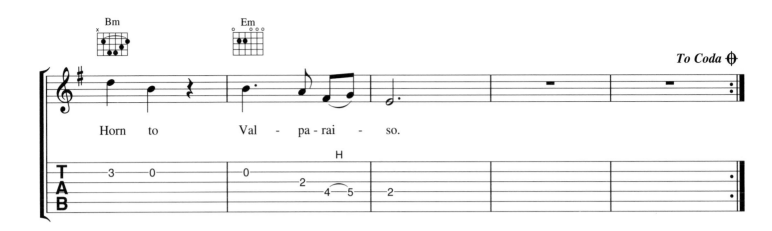

To Coda ⊕

Horn   to   Val   - pa - rai   -   so.

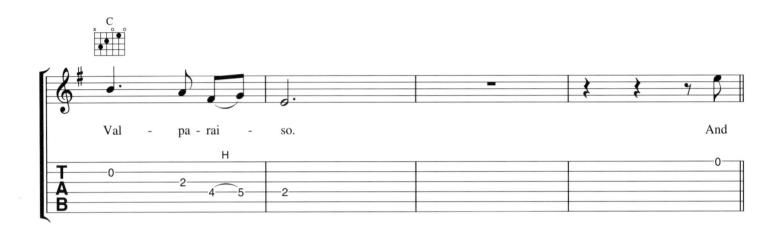

Val   - pa - rai   -   so.   And

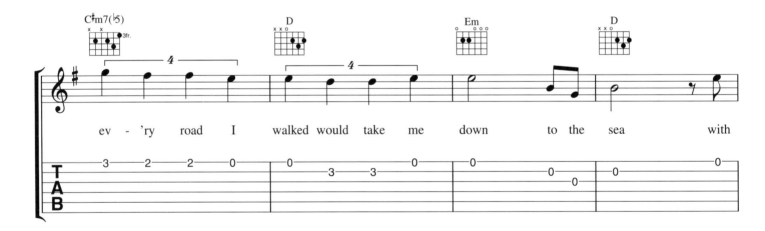

ev - 'ry   road   I   walked would   take   me   down   to   the   sea   with

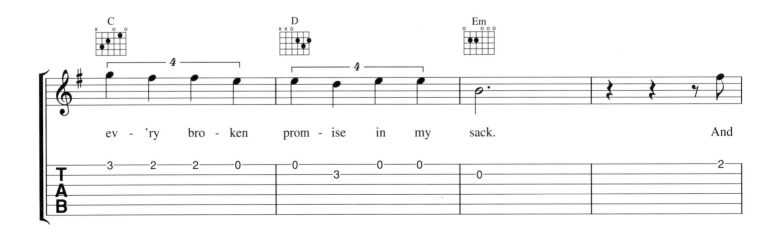

ev - 'ry   bro - ken   prom - ise   in   my   sack.   And

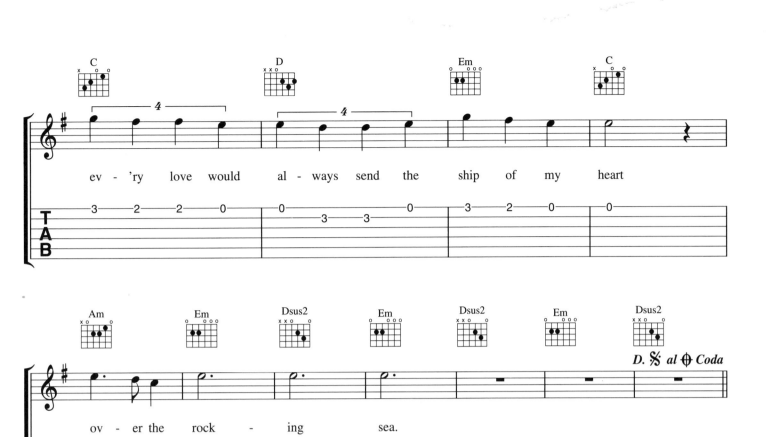

ev - 'ry love would al - ways send the ship of my heart

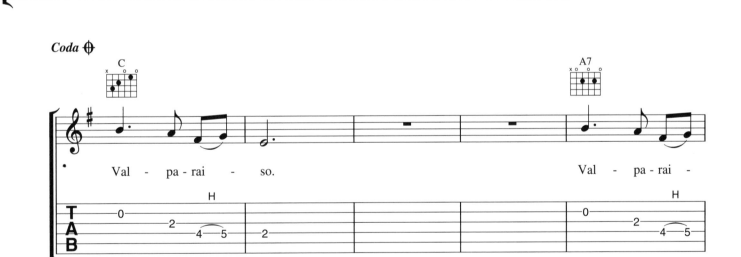

ov - er the rock - ing sea.

D. %al ⊕ Coda

Coda ⊕

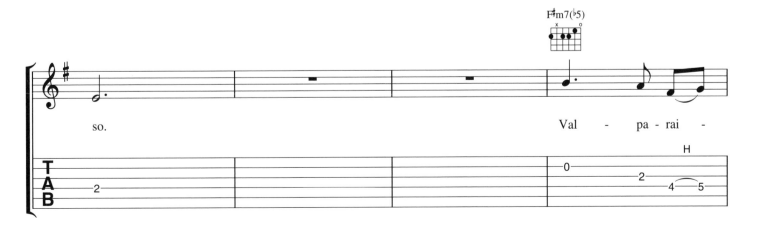

Val - pa - rai - so.   Val - pa - rai -

so.   Val - pa - rai -

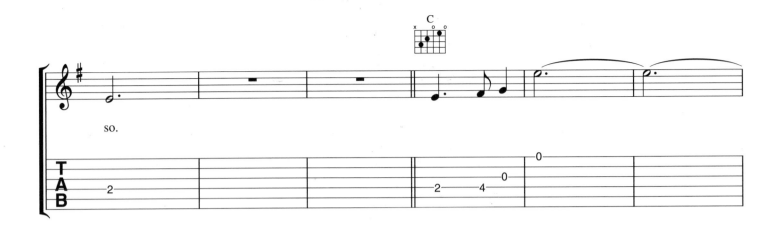

so.

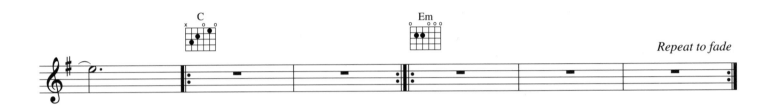

Repeat to fade

Verse 2

Red the port light,
Starboard the green.
How will she know of the devils I've seen?
Cross the sky,
Star of the sea,
Under the moonlight.
There she can safely go
Round the Cape Horn to Valparaiso.

Verse 3 (𝄋)

If I should die,
The water's my grave.
She'll never know if I'm damned or I'm saved.
See the ghost,
Over the sea,
Under the moonlight.
There she can safely to
Round the Cape Horn to Valparaiso.